Calculator Decision-Making Sourcebook

Second Edition

A collection of facts, examples, information, and techniques illustrating how you can use your *Advanced Professional Calculator* as a powerful decision-making tool in business, scientific and everyday life situations.

Note: The calculator keystrokes and descriptions in this book are based on the TI-55-II, with *Algebraic Operating System.* The facts, information and examples included will be useful when working with *any* calculator, but the keystroke sequences described will only be similar when using an advanced calculator with AOS entry system.

This book was developed by:

The Staff of the Texas Instruments Learning Center

Robert E. Whitsitt, II
Kathy A. Kelly
M. Dean LaMont
Dr. Ralph A. Oliva, Educational Software Director

And:

The Staff of the University of Denver Mathematics Laboratory
Dr. Ruth I. Hoffman, Director
Michael Zastrocky
James F. Reed
Dr. Sam Battaglia

With contributions by:

Samir W. Rizk
Lane L. Douglas
Charles L. McCollum
Harry Alderman
Dr. Paul Staiert
Dr. George Bardwell
Ross Wise
Joe Poyner

Artwork and layout were coordinated and executed by:

Gaither and Davy Design Inc.

And:

Deason and Schenck Associates

IMPORTANT

Texas Instruments makes no warranty, either express or implied, including but not limited to any implied warranties of merchantability and fitness for a particular purpose, regarding these book materials and makes such materials available solely on an "as-is" basis.

In no event shall Texas Instruments be liable to anyone for special, collateral, incidental, or consequential damages in connection with or arising out of the purchase or use of these materials and the sole and exclusive liability to Texas Instruments, regardless of the form of action, shall not exceed the purchase price of this book.

TABLE OF CONTENTS

TABLE OF CONTENTS

TABLE OF CONTENTS

π

TABLE OF CONTENTS (continued)

TABLE OF CONTENTS (continued) %

TABLE OF CONTENTS (continued)

Introduction

Hand-held calculators, such as the TI-55-II, have made mathematics easier. A new speed, confidence, and accuracy are now possible in handling the arithmetic parts of our lives. As hand-held calculators continue in their rapid evolution, advanced professional machines handling increasingly complicated mathematics are available. Many techniques that previously required large volumes of tables, tedious calculations, or access to a large computer center can now be carried out with a few keystrokes on a hand-held calculator.

This book discusses how the TI-55-II makes it easy for you to use the powerful statistical, mathematical, and scientific functions, concentrating on how to use these functions, stating them in a straightforward manner with examples and keystroke solutions. For those who want to know more about the details and theory, there is a brief survey of some of the basics of statistics.

The Story of Statistics

The science of statistics (as now known) traces its history to a gambler. In 1654 Antoine Gombaud, a young nobleman from France with the title of Chevalier de Méré, was concerned over his luck at the gaming tables. He sought advice and counsel from the noted French mathematician, Blaise Pascal. Among the problems he put to Pascal was the question of how prize money should be divided among the players if a game is interrupted for some reason.

This question led Pascal into the study of probabilities. Particularly he evaluated the probability of one given player winning if a cancelled game were continued to completion. Pascal wrote a letter about these problems and his work on games of chance to another famous French mathematician, Pierre de Fermat. The resulting exchange of letters was the beginning of the evolving science of statistics.

The Story of Calculators

Blaise Pascal was an interesting and productive man. While working with the science of probability and statistics, he also was working with what became one of the world's first "calculating machines" using the ideas of men such as John Napier. Pascal's work in this area began the evolution of the mechanical calculator. The first machines handled calculations rather slowly with the aid of complex entanglements of whirling gears, whizzing cranks, wheels, and windows. This evolution continued on up through 1890, when the punched card helped to take the 1890 U.S. Census. This led the way to later electric relay devices which continued to evolve into large-scale computers.

A few years ago, people working in the electronics industry made several breakthroughs that resulted in the integrated circuit (IC). Integrated circuits made it possible to process and store large amounts of information in very small spaces with little power and at low cost. These devices, coupled with the development of the inexpensive "Liquid Crystal Display" (LCD) made hand-held calculators a reality. Recent advances in integrated circuits are continuing to increase the amount of information storage and processing that can be handled on a single "IC chip". (The term "IC chip" refers to the tiny piece of silicon upon which an integrated circuit is fabricated.)

New highly flexible IC chips are making today's advanced professional and programmable hand-held calculators possible. With these advanced machines, highly complex mathematical calculations can be executed rapidly and accurately with the touch of a key.

The "Calculator Decision-Making Sourcebook"

Mathematics is part of many everyday, scientific, and business activities. Your calculator can quickly and accurately handle the mathematics side of life. Also, your advanced professional calculator can be a powerful ally as you make decisions. This book has been designed to show you how.

This book gives compact, accessible, step-by-step techniques enabling you to take a variety of decision-making situations and analyze them with keyboard solutions. The book was designed to work directly with the calculator, so be sure to use them together.

An important first step is to get thoroughly acquainted with your calculator, Chapter 1 of this book is a quick explanation of all the features and keys of the calculator, along with brief examples illustrating the use of each feature. Chapter 1 is divided into seven major sections:

Section 1 — Keyboard and Display Basics
Section 2 — Data Entry Keys
Section 3 — Algebraic Keys
Section 4 — Statistical Keys
Section 5 — Conversion Keys
Section 6 — Programming Keys
Section 7 — Integration

The subsequent chapters in the book give examples that illustrate how you can work with your machine in "Calculating Better Decisions." In each case a real life, business, mathematics, or science situation is analyzed for you.

Each example is broken down into the following segments; each identified with its own graphic symbol, as shown:

Target: A brief statement of what types of calculation are used to analyze the problem, and how to begin implementing the calculation.

Tools: The formulas and facts needed to solve the problem along with a brief statement as to why each is used, where the techniques come from, and how they are tailored to the specific example.

Keying it in: Sample keystrokes to execute the solution (using the data given in the example), along with what you'll see in the display at key points in the calculation.

Decision Time: How to use the results of the calculation in arriving at a conclusion or decision.

Going Further: For some examples, a "going further" section is included. It discusses how additional information or conclusions may be drawn from the calculation just completed.

While you're busy using your calculator, don't forget that even though it has the latest in solid-state technology, it still qualifies as a great toy for children of all ages. Play with it! Use it for exploring and "what iffing," as well as just idle doodling on the keys. You may just find yourself exploring patterns and relationships which can lead you to a new appreciation of the beautiful side of numbers and mathematics.

The Keys

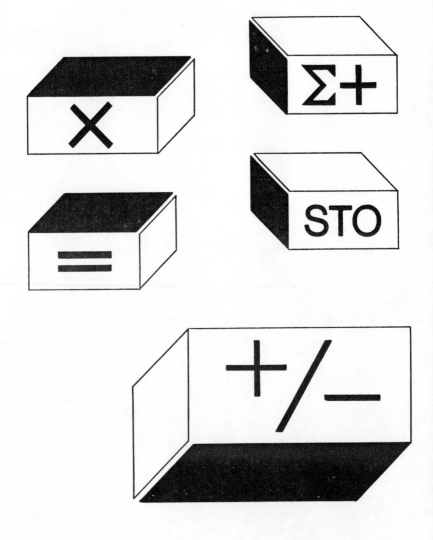

Introduction

Advanced professional calculators, such as the TI-55-II, are marvels made possible by the most recent breakthroughs in semiconductor technology. The integrated circuit, which made handheld calculators possible, appeared only a few years ago. The TI-55-II has many capabilities that make it the best choice for scientific applications. Its features include:

- **AOS™ Algebraic Operating System**

    Comprehensive data entry with the number and decimal keys, a π key, a key to exchange x and y values, and parentheses. Multiplication, division, addition and subtraction may be used with the Algebraic Operating System (which allows the entry of most problems as they are written) with up to four operations and 15 parentheses pending, and the results stored in up to eight user data memories. Data may be entered and displayed in standard format (with the necessary number of decimal places), in scientific format, and in engineering format.

- **Mathematical and Scientific Functions**

    Mathematical and scientific keys for all frequent needs, including reciprocal, square, square root, universal powers and roots, percent, percent change, factorial, signum, absolute value, fractional part, integer part, permutations, combinations, logarithms in both common and natural form, and all common trigonometric and hyperbolic functions and their inverses. Angular measures are displayed in degrees, radians, or grads, and are easily convertible from one to the other.

- **Statistical Functions**

    A full range of statistical keys, including simple data entry and correction with multiple data point capability, mean, and both population and sample standard deviation. Also available are keys for figuring linear-regression and trend-line problems, including correlation, slope, intercept, and one value given another.

- **Built-in Conversions**

  Conversion keys for degrees Fahrenheit to degrees Celsius, gallons to liters, pounds to kilograms, inches to centimeters, polar to rectangular coordinates, degrees/minutes/seconds to decimal degrees, and the reverse of each of these.

- **Straight-line Programming**

  A full range of programming keys, including run/stop, learn, reset, single step, backstep, insert, delete, and pause. Up to 56 programming steps may be in each program. Preprogrammed functions may be integrated.

With the TI-55-II you can solve problems and get information that previously would have required a giant computer. Any calculator, however, is no more functional than the knowledge of the person who operates it. By understanding all of its features and becoming completely acquainted with what it can (and cannot) do, you can solve problems and get information quickly and easily. This book is designed to explain, with many examples, what the TI-55-II calculator can do.

This chapter explains the essential features and keys of the calculator. Included is some information on why each key is important as well as how it is used.

The Sections of the chapter are listed below. If you are familiar with the basics of the calculator, you may want to go immediately to the application chapters.

Section 1—Keyboard and Display Basics
Section 2—Data Entry Keys
Section 3—Algebraic Keys
Section 4—Statistical Keys
Section 5—Conversion Keys
Section 6—Programming Keys
Section 7—Integration

Section 1—Keyboard and Display Basics

This Section is a quick explanation of the basics. Please keep the calculator with you so you can see the use of each feature as it is presented.

Turn the TI-55-II on with the [ON/c] key (at the top right of the keyboard). A zero appears in the display and a number of indicators may appear. If STAT is shown, press the key marked [2nd] (at the top left of the keyboard) and then the key marked [=] with **CSR** above it (at the lower right of the keyboard).

If PROG is displayed, press the key marked [2nd] (at the top left of the keyboard), the key marked [LRN] with **Part** above it (just below the key marked [2nd]), and the key marked [8] (near the center of the keyboard). Press the key marked [ON/c] again.

Press the key marked [2nd] (at the top left of the keyboard), and the key marked [3] with **CM** above it (near the lower right of the keyboard).

The display now shows a zero and a DEG indicator. The calculator is ready to perform all normal functions.

If the batteries are momentarily removed or replaced, clear the calculator by pressing [ON/c], [2nd] **Part** [8] → off, on/c, on/c, [2nd] **CM**, and [ON/c]. The display then shows 0 and DEG. 2nd CSR, 2nd Part 8

THE KEYBOARD

The calculator has many features that make calculations easy and accurate. To allow the use of all these features without crowding the keyboard, most of the keys have more than one function. Notice that most of the keys have symbols printed above them in addition to those on them. The symbols printed above the keys are second functions. To perform one of these functions, press the [2nd] key and then press the key for the function that you wish to perform. For example, to find the square root of 4.5, enter 4.5 and press [√x]. To find the square of 4.5, enter 4.5 and press [2nd] [x²]. Pressing the [2nd] key twice returns the following key to its first function.

In this book, keys for first functions are shown with black print on a white background. Keys with a black background are used to indicate second functions. For instance, to calculate squares, press [2nd] [x^2] .

The keys are grouped by function, with each group indicated by color. For example, some of the second functions are printed in orange. These are the functions used in statistical operations. The keys in the second row (and [R/S] in the first row) are connected with a blue band, and the second functions above them are printed in blue. These are the keys used in programming. All other second functions are printed in black.

The keys in the third and fourth rows (and [P→R] in the fifth row) are connected in gray, with the second functions printed in black. These are the keys that have an inverse function. To perform the inverse functions of these keys, press the [INV] key and then the key for the function. When [INV] is pressed before a function key, the calculator executes the inverse of the function indicated by that key. For example, pressing [INV] [sin] finds the arcsine ($\sin^{-1}$) of the number in the display. Pressing [INV] twice returns the following key to its non-inverse function.

The inverse function key can be used with the [2nd] function key. The keys [INV] and [2nd] may be used in any order in normal calculations, but must be [INV] followed by [2nd] in a program.

THE DISPLAY

Turn the calculator on with the [ON/C] key. The [ON/C] key is also used to clear entries and operations. If you are entering a number and make a mistake, press the [ON/C] key and reenter the number. *If an operation key has already been pressed, pressing the [ON/C] key clears all pending operations and operands entered. Pressing the [ON/C] key twice always clears the display and all pending operations and operands from the calculator.*

SECTION 1—KEYBOARD AND DISPLAY BASICS

The [ON/c] key is also used to clear the word "Error" from the display. "Error" appears any time that an error occurs because of the problem that is being solved. The most common instances of "Error" are in attempting to divide by zero, when taking the root or power of a negative number, and when exceeding the maximum or minimum number that the calculator can handle. See the Appendix for more information.

During calculations, the indicators are displayed and the digits disappear. This occurs briefly except when doing certain statistical problems and when running a program. During integration, the display briefly shows the value of the function at the end of each integration interval.

Turning the calculator off (with the [OFF] key) and back on (with the [ON/c] key) removes the number in the display and any pending calculations. Other numbers, in user data memories and in the programming or statistical registers, as well as the mode the calculator is in (statistics or programming) stay in the machine. The calculator always comes on in the degree mode.

The display shows eight digits, but the display register keeps 11 digits internally for use in calculations. Descriptions of the use of the value in the display refer to the 11 digits in the display register.

Statistics Mode Indicator

If STAT is displayed, the calculator is in the statistics mode. Because of the Constant Memory™ feature, the calculator retains the mode it was in when it was turned off. The statistics mode is set when [Σ+] or [2nd] [Frq] is pressed. [2nd] [CSR] clears the statistical registers and STAT indicator, and sets the partition to eight user data memories. The STAT mode is also cleared if there is an error due to the data when determining the mean, correlation, slope, intercept, or standard deviation. See the Appendix for more information.

Programming Mode Indicator

If PROG is displayed, the calculator is in the programming mode and there is space in the calculator's memory for a program. The calculator retains the mode that it was in when it was turned off and keeps any program that was in the program memory. The programming mode is entered by setting the partitioning to one to seven user data memories with the 2nd Part key. It is left by setting the partitioning to eight user data memories, or by entering the statistics mode. The programming keys are disabled in the statistics mode, so the programming mode may not be entered from the statistics mode.

Angular Mode Indicators

DEG indicates degree mode, RAD indicates radian mode, and GRAD indicates grad mode. The angular units may be changed with the DRG, INV DRG, 2nd DRG►, and INV 2nd DRG► keys. The calculator always returns to the degree mode when it is turned off and back on.

APD™ AUTOMATIC POWER DOWN

To conserve power, after 15 to 35 minutes of nonuse the calculator is automatically powered down through the APD™ feature. However, just turning it back on allows you to continue in the state the calculator was in, and use the values in the user data memories, statistics registers, and any stored program. Any pending operations and intermediate values are lost. The effect is the same as if you had pressed the OFF key.

Section 2 — Data Entry Keys

The following keys are used in entering, removing, and manipulating data to be used in subsequent calculations.

⓪ - ⑨ — DIGIT KEYS

The digit keys allow any number to be entered into the display in a logical left-to-right order.

⌷ — DECIMAL POINT KEY

The calculator operates with a floating decimal point which can be placed wherever needed. The decimal point is not displayed for integer numbers. A zero precedes the decimal point for numbers less than one. Zeros trailing the last significant digit on the right of a decimal point are not displayed unless the 2nd Fix key has been used to fix the number of decimal places displayed.

+/− — CHANGE SIGN KEY

Pressing the change sign key instructs the calculator to change the sign of the displayed value. This allows the use of negative numbers in calculations.

π — PI KEY

The π key enters the value of pi to 11 significant digits, with a value of 3.1415926536. The display shows the value of pi rounded to eight digits, or 3.1415927.

ON/C, 2nd CM, 2nd CP, 2nd CSR — CLEARING KEYS

The ON/C key is used to clear entries and operations. If a mistaken number is entered, press the ON/C key and reenter the number. *If an operation key has already been pressed, pressing the ON/C key clears all pending operations and the operands entered. Pressing the ON/C key twice always clears the display and all pending operations and operands from the calculator.* The user data memories, program registers, and statistical registers are not affected by this key.

The 2nd CM key clears the values from all user data memories. It does not affect a program or data in the statistical registers.

SECTION 2 — DATA ENTRY KEYS

The [2nd] [CP] key clears the current program and resets to step 00 so that a new one can be entered. As a safety feature, it only works in the learn mode so that a program cannot be accidentally cleared while in some other mode.

The [2nd] [CSR] key clears the statistical registers (memories 3 through 7) and the STAT indicator. It sets the partitioning to no program steps and eight user data memories. As a safety feature, it only works in the STAT mode so that the memories cannot be cleared while in some other mode.

The following table shows the effects of the clearing keys.

Effect of Clearing Keys

Key Pressed	Display Digits	Display Indicators	Pending Operations	User Data Memories	Program	Statistical Registers
[ON/c]	Cleared	None	None	None	None	None
[ON/c] [ON/c]	Cleared	None	Cleared	None	None	None
[2nd] [CM]	None	None	None	Cleared	None	None
[2nd] [CP]	None	None	None	None	Cleared	None
[2nd] [CSR]	None	Removes STAT	None	None	None	Cleared

[+], [−], [×], [÷], [=] — ARITHMETIC KEYS

The basic arithmetic operations of addition, subtraction, multiplication and division are performed with these five keys. The equals key completes all pending operations and readies the calculator for new calculations.

Several operations can be combined in one expression and entered into the calculator as written from left to right. The calculator has a special feature called the Algebraic Operating System to sort the operations and perform them in the correct order.

SECTION 2 — DATA ENTRY KEYS

AOS™ ALGEBRAIC OPERATING SYSTEM

The AOS™ Algebraic Operating System allows entering numbers and combined operations into the calculator in the same order in which they are written mathematically. Combined operations are performed following the universally accepted rules of the algebraic hierarchy which assign priorities to the various mathematical operations. Without such a fixed set of rules, expressions with several operations could have more than one correct interpretation. For example, the expression

$5 + 4 \times 3 - 2$

could have several different results. However, the rules of the algebraic hierarchy state that multiplications and divisions should be performed before additions and subtractions. Using these priorities, the calculator finds the correct solution is 15. The complete algebraic hierarchy, in descending order of priority, is:

1. The following perform the indicated function on the displayed value immediately: trigonometric, hyperbolic, square, square root, factorial, exponential, reciprocal, conversion, absolute value, integer, fractional part, signum, combinations, permutations, percent, and logarithmic keys
2. The percent change key
3. The universal powers and roots keys
4. Multiplication and division keys
5. Addition and subtraction keys
6. The equals key ⌷=⌷ completes all pending operations

NOTE: The following keys remove any pending calculations:
[2nd] [P↔R] ; [Σ+] ; [2nd] [Σ−] ; [2nd] [Mean] ; [2nd] [σn] ; [2nd] [σn-1] ; and [2nd] [b/a] .

The keys on the right side of the calculator are positioned to help you to remember the AOS™ hierarchy.

[y^x]
[÷]
[X]
[−]
[+]
[=]

Operations with the same priority in an expression are performed left to right. To illustrate the Algebraic Operating System, consider this example.

$$4 \div 5^2 \times 7 + 3 \times .5^{\cos 60°} = 3.2413203$$

Press	Display	Comments
[ON/C] [ON/C]	0	Clear display and pending operations
4 [÷] 5	5	The division is pending
[2nd] [x^2]	25	Special function [2nd] [x^2] is performed immediately
[X]	0.16	First division performed
7 [+]	1.12	Multiplication performed, addition pending
3 [X]	3	Second multiplication pending
.5 [y^x]	0.5	Universal exponential pending
60 [cos]	0.5	Special function performed immediately
[=]	3.2413203	Equals sign completes all pending operations

NOTE: If an incorrect operation is entered while there are pending calculations, it is safest to press [ON/C] [ON/C] and restart the problem.

[$x{:}y$] — X EXCHANGE Y KEY

In some calculating situations, the roles of x and y may be reversed after they have been entered. This key can be used to reverse the factors in multiplication, the divisor and dividend in division, or x and y in Δ%, y^x, and $\sqrt[x]{y}$. It is also used in statistical calculations and polar to rectangular conversions, discussed later.

[( ], [ )] — PARENTHESES KEYS

Some calculations require specifying the exact order in which numbers and operations are to be grouped. Placing a series of numbers and operations in parentheses indicates that they are to be evaluated first instead of in the order directed by the normal algebraic hierarchy. Within each set of parentheses, the calculator operates according to the rules of the algebraic hierarchy. Use the parentheses if there is any doubt about how the calculator will handle an expression.

SECTION 2 — DATA ENTRY KEYS

Example: $7 \times (3 + 4) = 49$

Press	Display	Comments
[ON/c] [ON/c]	0	Clear display and pending operations
7 [×] [( ] 3 [+] 4 [ )]	7	Addition result, multiplication pending
[=]	49	Result

The open parenthesis has the additional capability of supplying a missing number.

Example: $4 - (4 + 2) = -2$

Press	Display	Comments
[ON/c] [ON/c]	0	Clear display and pending operations
4 [−] [( ] [+]	4	Enters the number 4. The open parenthesis followed by a [+] causes the 4 to be repeated
2 [ )] [=]	−2	Answer

The close parenthesis does not supply a missing number. It does, however, complete the operation started with the most recent open parenthesis. If no open parenthesis is pending, the close parenthesis completes all pending operations.

There are limits to how many operations and associated numbers can be pending. As many as fifteen parentheses can be open at any one time and four operations can be pending, but only in the most complex situations will these limits be approached.

You may see equations or expressions written with parentheses used to indicate implied multiplication: $(2+1)(3+2) = 15$. The calculator does not perform implied multiplications. You must enter the multiplication sign.

[( ] 2 [+] 1 [ )] [×] [( ] 3 [+] 2 [ )] [=]

Here is an example on using parentheses.

Example: Evaluate $\dfrac{(8 + 9) \times -19}{(3 + 10) \div 7} = -173.92308$

In problems of this type, the calculator must evaluate the entire numerator, then divide by the entire denominator. To be sure that this takes place, add an extra set of parentheses around the numerator and denominator.

Press	Display	Comments
ON/C ON/C	0	Clear display and pending operations
((8 + 9) X	17	(8 + 9) displayed
19 +/−) ÷	−323	The value of the numerator
((3 + 10		
) ÷ 7)	1.8571429	The value of the denominator
=	−173.92308	The result

2nd K —CONSTANT KEY

The 2nd K key stores a number and an operation for use in repetitive calculations. Once the number and operation are stored, key in the numbers you want them to work on, press =, and the answer is displayed. Calculations using the 2nd K feature can be repeated as often as needed. Here is how it works.

- Enter the operation
- Enter the repetitive number m
- Press 2nd K
- Press =

From then on

- Enter the number to be operated on
- Press =

SECTION 2 — DATA ENTRY KEYS

The [2nd] [K] feature works in the following way with certain operations keys on the calculator.

[+] m [2nd] [K] [=]	adds m to each subsequent entry
[−] m [2nd] [K] [=]	subtracts m from each subsequent entry
[X] m [2nd] [K] [=]	multiplies each subsequent entry by m
[÷] m [2nd] [K] [=]	divides each subsequent entry by m
[yˣ] m [2nd] [K] [=]	raises each subsequent entry to the mth power, giving y^m
[INV] [yˣ] m [2nd] [K] [=]	takes the mth root of each subsequent entry, giving $\sqrt[m]{y}$
[2nd] [Δ%] m [2nd] [K] [=]	calculates the percentage change between each subsequent entry s and m, computing $\dfrac{s - m}{m} \times 100$.

You may enter [2nd] [K] while doing the first in the series of problems.

Example: Multiply 2, 4, 6, and 8 by π.

Press	Display	Comments
[ON/C] [ON/C]	0	Clear display and pending operations
2 [X] [π] [2nd] [K]	3.1415927	π
[=]	6.2831853	2π
4 [=]	12.566371	4π
6 [=]	18.849556	6π
8 [=]	25.132741	8π

Pressing [ON/C] after [=], [OFF], any of the above operations keys, or the close parenthesis key removes the automatic constant.

DISPLAY FORMATS

Even though the calculator has a display and entry limit of eight digits, the internal display register holds calculated results to 11 digits for greater accuracy in following calculations. The value displayed is rounded to eight digits.

In addition to the standard eight-digit floating decimal display, there are several other display formats available to increase the versatility of the calculator.

EE —Scientific Notation Key

Many scientific and engineering calculations involve very large or small numbers which can be awkward to manipulate. Scientific notation makes these values easier to handle. Any number can be expressed in scientific notation as a base value (mantissa) times 10 raised to some power (exponent). For example, the value 1,050,000 is expressed as 1.05×10^6 in scientific notation. The sign (+ or −) of the exponent indicates where the decimal point is placed when the number is written in standard form. A positive exponent indicates that the decimal is shifted to the right to display the number in standard format, and a negative exponent indicates that it is shifted to the left. The value of the exponent gives the number of places the decimal point is to be moved. The following table shows some numbers expressed in both standard form and scientific notation.

Standard Notation	Scientific Notation
6,789	6.789×10^3
.0000000021	2.1×10^{-9}
−16,389,043	-1.6389043×10^7
8.775	8.775×10^0

Your calculator's scientific notation allows you to use numbers as small as $\pm 1 \times 10^{-99}$ and as large as $\pm 9.9999999 \times 10^{99}$. Numbers smaller than $\pm 1 \times 10^{-7}$ and larger than $\pm 9.9999999 \times 10^7$ must be entered into the calculator in scientific notation. If calculations exceed these limits, the results are automatically displayed in scientific notation.

To enter a number in scientific notation, first enter the mantissa, pressing +/− if it is negative. Press EE and "00" appears at the right of the display. Then enter the exponent, pressing +/− if it is negative. If you press a wrong digit key when entering the exponent, press the correct digits and the calculator replaces the old digits with the last digits entered.

Example: Suppose you wanted to enter 6.023×10^{23} but accidentally press the exponent digits in the reverse order.

Press	Display	Comments
ON/c ON/c	0	Clear display and pending operations
6.023 EE 32	**6.023 32**	The exponent digits are reversed
3	**6.023 23**	The new entry shifts the exponents and corrects the error

Regardless of how a mantissa is entered in scientific notation, the calculator normalizes the number, displaying a single digit to the left of the decimal point, when any function or operation key is pressed.

After pressing the EE key, all results are displayed in scientific notation. To remove the scientific notation format or convert a number to standard form, press INV EE. Scientific notation is also removed by INV 2nd Eng, ON/c, or turning the calculator off and back on. If the number displayed is outside the range $\pm 1 \times 10^{-7}$ to $\pm 9.9999999 \times 10^{7}$, the calculator returns to the standard format only when a calculated result or entry is in the displayable range.

Example: Enter 32.5×10^{4} in scientific notation and change it to standard notation.

Press	Display	Comments
ON/c ON/c	0	Clear display and pending operations
32.5 EE 4	**32.5 04**	Entry
=	**3.25 05**	Scientific notation
INV EE	**325000**	Standard notation

SECTION 2 — DATA ENTRY KEYS

Data entered in standard form may be mixed with data in scientific notation for quicker calculations. The calculator converts the standard numbers and displays the results in scientific notation.

Example: $3.2 \times 10^3 + 12575.321 = 15775.321$

Press	Display	Comments
[ON/c] [ON/c]	0	Clear display and pending operations
3.2 [EE] 3	3.2 03	Enter first number
[+] 12575.321	12575.321	Add second number
[=]	1.5775321 04	Result in scientific notation
[INV] [EE]	15775.321	Convert result to standard notation

[2nd] [Eng] — Engineering Notation Key

Engineering notation is a modified form of scientific notation that allows easier interpretation of technical calculations. Numbers expressed in engineering notation are displayed as a mantissa times 10 raised to a power that is a multiple of three. This allows more convenient handling of metric and engineering units such as kilometers (meters $\times 10^3$), megawatts (watts $\times 10^6$), and milliseconds (seconds $\times 10^{-3}$).

After pressing the [2nd] [Eng] key, all results are displayed in engineering notation. Regardless of how a number is entered (standard format or scientific notation), the calculator normalizes the number, displaying an exponent which is a multiple of three and a mantissa with one, two, or three digits to the left of the decimal point, when any function or operation key is pressed. To remove the engineering notation format or convert a number to standard form, press [INV] [2nd] [Eng]. If the number displayed is outside the range $\pm 1 \times 10^{-7}$ to $\pm 9.9999999 \times 10^7$, the calculator displays the number in scientific notation and returns to the standard format only when a result or entry is in the displayable range. Engineering notation is also removed by turning the calculator off and back on.

Example: Enter 32.5 × 10⁴ in engineering notation and change it to standard notation.

Press	Display	Comments
ON/C ON/C	0	Clear display and pending operations
32.5 EE 4	32.5 04	Entry
2nd Eng	325 03	Set engineering notation
INV 2nd Eng	325000	Standard notation

2nd Fix n—Fix Decimal Key

In some calculations you may wish to display a fixed number of digits following the decimal point in standard, scientific, or engineering notation. Pressing 2nd Fix n directs the calculator to round the display to n decimal places. The internal display register still retains the full 11 digit accuracy for use in subsequent calculations.

Fixed decimal format can be used in conjunction with either scientific or engineering notation. When used with these, 2nd Fix n sets the number of decimal places displayed in the mantissa.

If the calculator is in the standard fixed-decimal format and a calculated result exceeds $\pm 9.9999999 \times 10^7$ or goes below $\pm 1 \times 10^{-7}$, the display automatically converts to scientific notation and the fixed-decimal format is ignored. The display returns to the fixed-decimal format when scientific notation is no longer necessary.

Reset the calculator to the floating decimal point with INV 2nd Fix, 2nd Fix 8, 2nd Fix 9, or by turning the calculator off and back on.

Example: Display 500÷3, rounded to 6, 2, and 0 decimal places, in both standard notation and scientific notation. Then return to standard notation with a floating decimal point.

Press	Display	Comments
ON/c ON/c	0	Clear display and pending operations
500 ÷ 3 =	166.66667	Result of division
2nd Fix 6	166.66667	Fix decimal to 6 places. Only 5 can be shown
2nd Fix 2	166.67	Fix decimal to 2 places
2nd Fix 0	167	Fix decimal to 0 places
INV 2nd Fix	166.66667	Restore floating decimal point
EE	1.6666667 02	Enter scientific notation
2nd Fix 6	1.666667 02	Fix decimal to 6 places
2nd Fix 2	1.67 02	Fix decimal to 2 places
2nd Fix 0	2 02	Fix decimal to 0 places
INV EE	167	Leave scientific notation
INV 2nd Fix	166.66667	Restore floating decimal point

Note that while the displayed value is rounded to the desired format, the internal value is unaffected.

MEMORY OPERATIONS

The calculator may have a maximum of eight user data memories, numbered 0 through 7, which can be used to store intermediate results or long values. The following keys and operations allow manipulation of the numbers in the user data memories. The number of user data memories is set with the 2nd Part key.

2nd CM — Clear Memories Key

The 2nd CM key clears the user data memories. The display, statistical registers, and program steps are not affected.

STO m — Store Memory Key

The STO m key stores the value shown in the display in user data memory m. For instance, the key sequence 3 STO 1 stores the value 3 in user data memory number 1.

SECTION 2 — DATA ENTRY KEYS

RCL m — Recall Memory Key

The RCL m key recalls to the display the number in user data memory m. For instance, the key sequence RCL 0 recalls to the display the number that was in user data memory number 0. The number that was in the display is lost.

EXC m — Exchange Memory Key

The EXC m key exchanges the value in the display with the value in user data memory m. For instance, the key sequence 3 EXC 2 stores the value 3 in user data memory number 2 and displays the value that was in user data memory number 2.

MEMORY ARITHMETIC

The results of calculations may be stored in a user data memory by entering a value, pressing STO, entering the operation to be performed, and entering the number of the user data memory in which to store the result. These key sequences are used to accumulate results from a series of independent calculations. The displayed number and calculations in progress are not affected. To use these sequences:

- Enter the number that is to operate on the memory value
- Press STO
- Enter the operation to be performed
- Enter the number of the memory to be used

NOTE: Because of the calculator's Constant Memory™ feature, the user data memories are not cleared when the calculator is turned off. Be sure to press ON/c STO m initially to clear the desired user data memory before using any of the following key sequences. 2nd CM clears all the user data memories defined by the current partitioning.

STO + m algebraically adds the displayed value to the contents of user data memory m.

STO − m algebraically subtracts the displayed value from the contents of user data memory m.

STO X m multiplies the contents of user data memory m by the displayed value.

[STO] [÷] m divides the contents of user data memory m by the displayed value.

[STO] [y^x] m raises the contents of user data memory m to the power in the display.

[STO] [INV] [y^x] m takes the root indicated by the number in the display of the value in user data memory m.

[STO] [2nd] [Δ%] m determines the percent change from the number in the display to the value in user data memory m.

Example:		
$28.3 \times 7 =$	198.1	
$173 + 16 =$	189	
$31 - 42 + 7.8 =$	−3.2	
Total	383.9	

Press	**Display**	**Comments**
[ON/C] [ON/C] [STO] 0	0	Clear display, pending operations, and memory 0
28.3 [X] 7 [=] [STO] [+] 0	198.1	Result of first problem added to user data memory 0
173 [+] 16 [=] [STO] [+] 0	189	Result of second problem added to user data memory 0
31 [−] 42 [+] 7.8 [=] [STO] [+] 0	−3.2	Result of third problem added to user data memory 0
[RCL] 0	383.9	Sum of the problems

Section 3 — ALGEBRAIC KEYS

The keys discussed in this Section all perform tasks that are frequently needed in algebraic operations.

NOTE: Limits on the range and accuracy of these keys are discussed in the Appendix.

[2nd] [|x|], [2nd] [Sgn], [2nd] [Intg], [2nd] [Frac] — NUMBER PORTION KEYS

[2nd] [|x|] calculates and displays the absolute value of the number in the display. The absolute value of a number is the magnitude of the number, regardless of its sign. Thus the result of [2nd] [|x|] is always a positive number.

[2nd] [Sgn] applies the signum function to the value displayed. If the number is negative, then −1 is put in the display. If the number is zero or positive, then 1 is put in the display.

[2nd] [Intg] displays the integer part of the number in the display register and discards the fractional part. See the following note.

[2nd] [Frac] displays the fractional part of the number in the display register and discards the integer part. See the following note.

NOTE: The [2nd] [Intg] and [2nd] [Frac] keys operate on the 11 internal digits in the display register, not the 8 digits shown in the display. This means that when [2nd] [Intg] is pressed and 4.9999999999 is in the display register internally (which rounds to a value of 5 in the display), that 4 will be the integer that remains in the display. Similarly, [2nd] [Frac] will give a display of 1, with the actual value being .9999999999.

[√x̄], [2nd] [x²] — SQUARE ROOT AND SQUARE KEYS

These keys find the square roots and squares of numbers. They act immediately on the number in the display and do not affect pending calculations.

The square root key [√x̄] calculates the square root of the positive number in the display. The square root of a number (x) is another number (labeled $\sqrt{x}$) such that $\sqrt{x}$ times $\sqrt{x}$ equals x.

[2nd] [x²] calculates the square of the number in the display, multiplying the displayed number by itself.

y^x, INV y^x — UNIVERSAL POWER AND ROOT KEYS

y^x is the universal power key. It raises any positive number to any power. To use this key:

- Enter the number to be raised to a power ("y")
- Press y^x
- Enter the power ("x")
- Press $=$

Example: Calculate $3.1897^{4.7343}$

Press	Display	Comments
ON/C ON/C	0	Clear display and pending operations
3.1897 y^x	3.1897	"y" value
4.7343	4.7343	"x" value
$=$	242.60674	Result: y^x

The universal root key takes any root of any positive number. To use this key:

- Enter the number to take the root of ("y")
- Press INV y^x
- Enter the root to be taken ("x")
- Press $=$

Example: Calculate $\sqrt[3.871]{21.496}$

Press	Display	Comments
ON/C ON/C	0	Clear display and pending operations
21.496 INV y^x	21.496	"y" value
3.871	3.871	"x" value
$=$	2.2089685	Result: $\sqrt[x]{y}$

[ln*x*] , [log] , [INV] [ln*x*] , [INV] [log] — LOGARITHM AND ANTILOGARITHM KEYS

Logarithms are mathematical functions used in a variety of technical and theoretical calculations. In addition, they form an important part of many mathematical "models" of natural phenomena. The logarithm keys give immediate access to the "log" of any number without having to locate it in a table.

The natural logarithm key [ln*x*] displays the natural logarithm (base e = 2.7182818) of the number in the display. The number in the display must be positive and greater than zero.

The common logarithm key [log] displays the common logarithm (base 10) of the number in the display. The number in the display must be positive and greater than zero.

The antilogarithm keys raise e and 10 to the power of the number in the display. [INV] [ln*x*] raises e to the power in the display. [INV] [log] raises 10 to the power in the display.

Example: Calculate log 15.32, ln 203.451, $e^{-.69315}$, 10^{π}

Press	Display	Comments
[ON/c] [ON/c]	0	Clear display and pending operations
15.32 [log]	1.1852588	
203.451 [ln*x*]	5.3154252	
.69315 [+/−] [INV] [ln*x*]	0.4999986	
[π] [INV] [log]	1385.4557	

[2nd] **1/*x*** — RECIPROCAL KEY

The reciprocal key [2nd] **1/*x*** divides the displayed number into one. For example, 4 [2nd] **1/*x*** equals 1/4 or .25.

[2nd] [x!], [2nd] [nPr], [2nd] [nCr] — FACTORIAL, PERMUTA-TIONS, AND COMBINATIONS KEYS

The factorial, permutations, and combinations keys act on the number in the display, and do not affect calculations in progress. The [2nd] [x!] key calculates and displays the factorial of the number. The factorial of any integer x is written x!, and is equal to (1 × 2 × 3 × ... × x). 0! is equal to 1 by definition. The calculator can determine the factorial of any integer less than 70.

The [2nd] [nPr] key determines the possible permutations (number of arrangements) of n items taken r at a time. This is usually written as $P\left(\begin{array}{c}n\\r\end{array}\right)$. The calculator actually calculates $\frac{n!}{(n-r)!}$.

The [2nd] [nCr] key determines the possible combinations of n items taken r at a time. This is usually written as $C\left(\begin{array}{c}n\\r\end{array}\right)$. The calculator actually calculates $\frac{n!}{(n-r)! \times r!}$.

The values of n and r are entered as n.rrr. For instance, to enter 5 items taken 2 at a time, enter 5.002. If you enter 5.02, the calculator determines 5 items taken 20 at a time. If you enter 5.2, the calculator determines 5 items taken 200 at a time. "Error" is displayed if r is entered as more than three digits.

Example: How many possible different thirteen card bridge hands are there? In this case n is 52 and r is 13.

Press	Display	Comments
[ON/C] [ON/C]	0	Clear display and pending operations
52.013 [2nd] [nCr]	6.3501356 11	Combinations

Example: The individual books of a 10 volume set of Shakespeare are placed next to each other on a shelf at random. How many possible orderings of the volumes are there? In this case n is 10 and r is 10.

Press	Display	Comments
[ON/C] [ON/C]	0	Clear display and pending operations
10.01 [2nd] [nPr]	3628800	Permutations

SECTION 3 — ALGEBRAIC KEYS

DRG, INV DRG, 2nd DRG►, INV 2nd DRG► — DEGREE, RADIAN, AND GRAD KEYS

The calculator handles a variety of calculations involving angles, such as the trigonometric functions and polar/rectangular conversions. When performing these calculations, select any one of the three common units for angular measure.

Degrees are each equal to $1 \div 360$ of a circle. A right angle equals 90°.

Radians are each equal to $1 \div 2\pi$ of a circle. A right angle equals $\pi \div 2$ radians.

Grads are each equal to $1 \div 400$ of a circle. A right angle equals 100 grads.

The calculator is always in degree mode when it is turned on, indicated by DEG in the display. Pressing DRG changes it to radian mode, indicated by RAD in the display. Pressing DRG again changes it to grad mode, indicated by GRAD in the display. Pressing DRG again returns the calculator to degree mode. You may also go through the modes in reverse order — from degrees to grads to radians and back to degrees — by pressing the INV DRG key.

The 2nd DRG► key changes the mode displayed, and additionally converts the number in the display to the new units. Thus 90 in the degree mode followed by 2nd DRG► changes the mode to radians and the display to 1.5707963 ($\pi \div 2$). Pressing 2nd DRG► again changes the mode to grads and the display to 100. You may also go through the modes and values in reverse order — from degrees to grads to radians and back to degrees — by pressing the INV 2nd DRG► key.

sin , cos , tan , INV sin , INV cos , INV tan — **TRIGONO-
METRIC KEYS**

The trigonometric keys sin , cos , and tan calculate the sine, cosine, and tangent of the angle in the display, with the angle
measured in the units selected with the DRG , INV DRG , 2nd DRG► , or
INV 2nd DRG► keys. The trigonometric functions relate the angles
and sides of a right triangle as shown below.

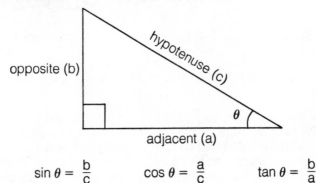

$$\sin \theta = \frac{b}{c} \qquad \cos \theta = \frac{a}{c} \qquad \tan \theta = \frac{b}{a}$$

The inverse functions of the trigonometric keys give the angle, in
the units selected, whose sine, cosine, or tangent is in the display.
INV sin calculates the arcsine ($\sin^{-1}$), INV cos calculates the arccosine ($\cos^{-1}$), and INV tan calculates the arctangent ($\tan^{-1}$).

Note the following ranges from the use of the inverse trigonometric
functions.

Arc Function	Range of Resultant Angle
arcsin x	0 to 90°, $\pi \div 2$ radians, or 100G
arcsin −x	0 to −90°, $-\pi \div 2$ radians, or −100G
arccos x	0 to 90°, $\pi \div 2$ radians, or 100G
arccos −x	90° to 180°, $\pi \div 2$ to π radians, or 100G to 200G
arctan x	0 to 90°, $\pi \div 2$ radians, or 100G
arctan −x	0 to −90°, $-\pi \div 2$ radians, or −100G

SECTION 3 — ALGEBRAIC KEYS

hyp — HYPERBOLIC FUNCTION KEY

Preceding one of the trigonometric keys with the hyp key calculates the hyperbolic sine (sinh), hyperbolic cosine (cosh), hyperbolic tangent (tanh), hyperbolic arcsine (sinh^{-1}), hyperbolic arccosine (cosh^{-1}), and hyperbolic arctangent (tanh^{-1}) of the number in the display. These functions operate in a fashion similar to the trigonometric functions except the angular mode (DEG, RAD, GRAD) has no effect on hyperbolic functions. The keys INV and hyp may be used together with either one first. The following illustrate the use of the hyperbolic function key.

Keys Pressed	Result
hyp sin	Hyperbolic sine (sinh)
INV hyp sin	Hyperbolic arcsine (arcsinh or sinh^{-1})
hyp INV sin	Hyperbolic arcsine (arcsinh or sinh^{-1})

NOTE: The key sequence hyp 2nd is the same as if just 2nd had been pressed. The key sequence 2nd hyp is the same as if just hyp had been pressed. Pressing hyp twice returns the following trigonometric function to its primary function.

Example: Find the hyperbolic tangent of $100 \div 3.3 \times 10^2$.

Press	Display	Comments
ON/c ON/c	0	Clear display and pending operations
100 ÷ 3.3 EE 2 =	3.030303−01	Intermediate result
hyp tan	2.940833−01	Answer in scientific notation
INV EE	0.2940833	Answer in standard notation

Note the following restrictions on the limits of the inverse hyperbolic functions:

Arcsinh x must have a value such that $-10^{50} < x < -10^{-50}$, $10^{-50} < x < 10^{50}$, x=0.
Arccosh x must have a value such that $1 \le x < 10^{50}$.
Arctanh x must have a value such that $-1 < x < 1$.

[2nd] **%** , [2nd] **Δ%** — **PERCENT AND PERCENT CHANGE KEYS**

These keys are useful for a wide variety of business and domestic percentage calculations.

The [2nd] **%** key converts the number in the display to a decimal percent by multiplying it by 0.01. If you enter 43.9 and press [2nd] **%** , 0.439 is displayed.

The real power of the [2nd] **%** key is demonstrated when it is used with an operation key. This allows "mark up" and "mark down" as well as straight and inverted percentage calculations. The rules for using the [2nd] **%** key in these situations are as follows.

m [+] n [2nd] **%** [=] adds n% of m to m
m [−] n [2nd] **%** [=] subtracts n% of m from m
m [×] n [2nd] **%** [=] multiplies m by n%
m [÷] n [2nd] **%** [=] divides m by n%

The [2nd] **Δ%** (change percent or delta percent) key calculates the percentage change between two values. This type of calculation is often used in business and everyday situations.

Example: Suppose your car has been getting 17.0 miles per gallon (call this x). After tuning it, mileage increases to 19.8 MPG (y). What is the percent increase?

To calculate this, enter y, press [2nd] **Δ%**, enter x, press [=], and the percentage change is displayed. (The calculator figures $\frac{y - x}{x} \times 100$.)

Press	**Display**	**Comments**
[ON/C] [ON/C]	0	Clear display and pending operations
19.8 [2nd] **Δ%**	19.8	Enter new mileage (y)
17	17	Enter old mileage (x)
[=]	16.470588	Percent change

Section 4 — Statistical Keys

In many situations in business and everyday life, you may find yourself handling a set of data points. This data may be test scores, sales figures, weights of an incoming shipment, etc. The most common statistical calculations used to understand the meaning of that data are the mean and standard deviation. The mean (or average) value is the central tendency of the data. The standard deviation shows how variable the data are — how far the data tend to differ from the mean.

The calculator has special features that allow you to enter data quickly and calculate the mean and standard deviation. Here is the procedure:

- Begin any statistical calculations with [ON/c] [ON/c] [2nd] [CSR], to clear the display, pending operations, and the statistical registers.
- Enter each data point, then press the [Σ+] key. If you make a mistake, remove the data point by rekeying the error and pressing [2nd] [Σ-]. (Refer to the table at the end of this Section.) To enter the same data point up to 99 times, use the [2nd] [Frq] key. You may enter a total of up to 99,999 data points.
- NOTE: As you enter the data, the calculator displays the number of data points that have been entered.

When all data points are entered:

- Press [2nd] [Mean] to display the mean value of the data.
- Press [2nd] [σn-1] or [2nd] [σn] to calculate the standard deviation for the data. The [2nd] [σn-1] key is used when a sample taken from the population has been entered. The [2nd] [σn] key is used when the entire population has been entered.

STANDARD DEVIATION

For convenience, the option has been provided to select n weighting (with the [2nd] [σn] key) or $n-1$ weighting (with the [2nd] [σn-1] key) when finding the standard deviation. The [2nd] [σn] key results in a maximum likelihood estimator that is generally used to describe populations, while the [2nd] [σn-1] key is an unbiased estimator customarily used for sampled data.

LINEAR REGRESSION

Linear regression provides a way to deal with one of the oldest problems in the world; predicting the future. With the linear regression keys on the calculator you can use data about past performances or relations to make forecasts of future performance (assuming that whatever relationship is at work continues). Chapter 3 explains in detail how to use the linear regression keys.

Knowledge of the detailed statistical theory behind the use and functions of these keys and features is beyond the scope of this book. In this Section, these functions are shown with step-by-step procedures. Later chapters give examples illustrating how to use these keys in everyday, scientific, and business applications. It is not necessary to have a detailed background in statistics to use the tools the calculator provides. If you would like a brief review of some of the theory behind these keys, see Chapter 8.

Examples of the use of some of these keys follow the descriptions. More examples are found in Chapter 3.

In linear regression, data is usually expressed as pairs of variables that could be plotted on a graph. The points are usually labeled with the letters (x,y). "x" may be dollars spent for advertising while "y" is sales, or "x" may be a test score and "y" a performance record, etc. You want to make a prediction: For any given "x" value, what is the predicted value of "y", and vice versa? The calculator determines the best straight line through the data points. You may then use the straight line to make predictions. Here are the steps to do this:

- Begin linear regression calculations with [ON/c] [ON/c] [2nd] [CSR], to clear the display, pending operations, and the statistical registers.
- Enter an "x" value and press [x≷y].
- Enter the corresponding "y" value and press [Σ+].
- The [2nd] [Frq] key can be used to enter duplicate "x" and "y" values just as in statistics problems. Refer to the table at the end of this Section.
- Continue until all data points are entered.

The calculator is now ready to draw the best straight line through the points and give the slope and intercept, and to give an "x'" for a "y" you enter or a "y'" for an "x" you enter.

See the note after the explanation of (2nd) **y'** and (2nd) **x'**.

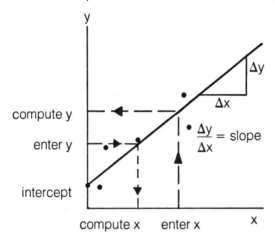

TREND LINE ANALYSIS

Trend line calculations are the same as linear regression calculations except that the "x" values increment by one for each "y" value entered. You may enter the first value; otherwise a value of 0 is used as a starting point for the "x" values if (ON/C) (ON/C) is pressed before starting the trend line analysis entry. The calculator automatically increments the "x" values by 1 as "y" values are entered.

The (2nd) **Σ-** key does not decrement the "x" value, so errors in entry require reentry of all data.

THE STATISTICS KEYS

NOTE: Statistical functions use 5 of the calculator's memories, numbers 3 through 7. They are automatically cleared when the statistics mode is entered with (Σ+) or (2nd) **Frq**. To leave the statistics mode, press the (2nd) **CSR** key.

(2nd) **CSR** — Clear Statistical Registers Key

*To return the calculator to normal calculation mode from statistics mode, press the (2nd) **CSR** key. The STAT indicator in the display is removed, indicating the calculator has eight user data memories with memories 3 through 7 cleared.*

Σ+ , x:y Σ+ , 2nd Σ− , x:y 2nd Σ− , 2nd Frq — **Statistics Data Entry Keys**

These keys are used to enter data points in statistics, linear regression, and trend line analysis calculations. The first time the Σ+ or 2nd Frq key is used, the calculator enters the statistics mode, displays STAT, clears memories 3 through 7, and removes any program which may have been in the calculator. The Σ+ and x:y Σ+ keys are used to enter data points, and the 2nd Σ− and x:y 2nd Σ− keys are used to remove data points.

When several identical data points are to be entered, enter them with the 2nd Frq ff Σ+ and x:y 2nd Frq ff Σ+ keys, and remove them with the 2nd Frq ff 2nd Σ− and x:y 2nd Frq ff 2nd Σ− keys. Note that the Σ+ and 2nd Frq keys clear any pending operations.

2nd Mean , 2nd Mean x:y — **Mean Keys**

The 2nd Mean key gives the mean of the "y" values entered. Then pressing x:y gives the mean of the "x" values entered. Note that the 2nd Mean key removes any pending operations.

2nd σn-1 , 2nd σn , 2nd σn-1 x:y , 2nd σn x:y , — **Standard Deviation Keys**

The 2nd σn-1 and 2nd σn keys give the sample and population standard deviation of the y data points that have been entered. The 2nd σn-1 x:y and 2nd σn x:y keys give the sample and population standard deviation of the x data points that have been entered.

The difference between the sample standard deviation (2nd σn-1 and 2nd σn-1 x:y) and the population standard deviation (2nd σn and 2nd σn x:y) becomes very small for over 30 data points. A population is usually a large set of items, and a sample is a smaller portion selected from the population. There is more about these terms in later chapters of the book. Note that the 2nd σn-1 , 2nd σn , 2nd σn-1 x:y , and 2nd σn x:y keys remove any pending operations.

SECTION 4 — STATISTICAL KEYS

[2nd] [Corr] — Correlation Key

The [2nd] [Corr] key gives the correlation between the "x" and "y" values. A value near 1 indicates that the values are very closely related. A value near 0 indicates that the values are only slightly related. A value near −1 indicates that the values are very closely related, but in a negative way, that is, an increase in one is related to a decrease in the other.

[2nd] [b/a], [2nd] [b/a] [x:y] — Intercept and Slope Keys

The [2nd] [b/a] key displays the intercept of the line the calculator determined was the best line through the points entered. Pressing the [x:y] key then displays the slope of the line. Note that the [2nd] [b/a] and [2nd] [b/a] [x:y] keys remove any pending operations.

[2nd] [y'], [2nd] [x'] — Predicted Value Keys

After entering an "x" value, pressing the [2nd] [y'] key displays the "y" value that corresponds with that "x" on the line that the calculator determined was the best line through the points. Similarly, following a "y" value with [2nd] [x'] gives the corresponding "x" value.

NOTE: Caution should be used in computing an "x" (independent) value on the basis of a "y" (dependent) value. Further, it is not valid to compute a "y" value on the basis of an "x" which is outside the range of the entered "x" values. The predictions which result do not have statistical validity, and the probability figures that are found are not valid. However, trend line analysis and forecasting calculations often use these computations to make predictions or estimations of probability about the future. When performing such calculations, the actual values may differ from the calculated values.

STATISTICS EXAMPLES

Example: You are teaching a course and the first set of test scores is as shown below.

96	65	81	85	76	86	57	98
75	78	100	72	81	70	80	

What are the mean and standard deviation of these scores?

Keying it in: Enter all the scores with the ⟮Σ+⟯ key. Then find the mean and standard deviation with the ⟮2nd⟯ ⟮Mean⟯ and ⟮2nd⟯ ⟮σn⟯ keys.

Press	Display	Comments
⟮ON/c⟯ ⟮ON/c⟯ ⟮2nd⟯ ⟮CSR⟯	0	Clear display and pending operations. If necessary, clear statistics registers
96 ⟮Σ+⟯	1	The STAT indicator appears in the display
65 ⟮Σ+⟯	2	The calculator counts the data points
81 ⟮Σ+⟯ 85 ⟮Σ+⟯	4	
76 ⟮Σ+⟯ 86 ⟮Σ+⟯	6	
57 ⟮Σ+⟯ 98 ⟮Σ+⟯	8	
75 ⟮Σ+⟯ 78 ⟮Σ+⟯	10	
100 ⟮Σ+⟯ 72 ⟮Σ+⟯	12	
81 ⟮Σ+⟯ 70 ⟮Σ+⟯	14	
80 ⟮Σ+⟯	15	
⟮2nd⟯ ⟮Mean⟯	80	Class average
⟮2nd⟯ ⟮σn⟯	11.564313	Standard deviation

SECTION 4 — STATISTICAL KEYS

Example: Suppose you have received a shipment of cans that are supposed to contain 4 liters of paint each. The volumes of a sample selected from the shipment are as follows.

1 can with a volume of 3.7 liters.
3 cans with a volume of 3.8 liters.
5 cans with a volume of 3.9 liters.
9 cans with a volume of 4.0 liters.
8 cans with a volume of 4.1 liters.
3 cans with a volume of 4.2 liters.
1 can with a volume of 4.3 liters.

What is the mean and standard deviation?

Keying it in: All 30 volumes could be entered using the ⟨Σ+⟩ key, but it is faster to use the ⟨2nd⟩ ⟨Frq⟩ key.

Press	Display	Comments
⟨ON/c⟩ ⟨ON/c⟩ ⟨2nd⟩ ⟨CSR⟩	0	Clear display, pending operations, and statistical registers
3.7 ⟨Σ+⟩	1	Enter first value. STAT appears in the display
3.8 ⟨2nd⟩ ⟨Frq⟩	Fr 00	Enter second value and frequency mode
3	Fr 03	Enter frequency value
⟨Σ+⟩	4	Number of values entered
3.9 ⟨2nd⟩ ⟨Frq⟩ 5 ⟨Σ+⟩	9	Continue entry until all
4 ⟨2nd⟩ ⟨Frq⟩ 9 ⟨Σ+⟩	18	points have been entered
4.1 ⟨2nd⟩ ⟨Frq⟩ 9 ⟨Σ+⟩	27	Incorrect frequency entered
4.1 ⟨2nd⟩ ⟨Σ−⟩	26	Incorrect value removed
4.2 ⟨2nd⟩ ⟨Frq⟩ 3 ⟨Σ+⟩	29	
4.3 ⟨Σ+⟩	30	
⟨2nd⟩ ⟨Mean⟩	4.01	Average volume
⟨2nd⟩ ⟨σn-1⟩	0.1373392	Standard deviation

Example: Suppose that you have been keeping records of the amount of rainfall each July in your city for the last five years. Can you use this data to predict the amount of rainfall this July? The data you have are shown below.

Year	Rainfall in centimeters
1976	8.6
1977	11.2
1978	11.0
1979	4.1
1980	5.3

Keying it in:

Press	Display	Comments
ON/C ON/C 2nd CSR	0	Clear display, pending operations, and statistical registers
1976 x:y 8.6 Σ+	1	Enter first year and rainfall
11.2 Σ+	2	The x value is automatically incremented by one, to 1977
11 Σ+ 4.1 Σ+	4	
5.3 Σ+	5	
2nd Corr	−0.6677606	The correlation shows that rainfall per year is decreasing. −0.67 is not a very significant correlation
1981 2nd y'	3.9299999	The predicted rainfall

SECTION 4 — STATISTICAL KEYS

PROCEDURES TO ENTER AND OBTAIN STATISTICAL DATA

The procedures to enter and remove an array of data are shown in the following chart.

SINGLE-VARIABLE DATA	TWO-VARIABLE DATA
1. To Enter Single Occurrence Data Points	
• Enter data point • Press Σ+ • Repeat for next data point	• Enter "x" data point • Press x:y • Enter "y" data point • Press Σ+ • Repeat for next data point
2. To Remove Single Occurrence Data Points Entered	
• Press ON/c x:y • Enter unwanted data point • Press 2nd Σ−	• Enter unwanted "x" data point • Press x:y • Enter unwanted "y" data point • Press 2nd Σ−
3. To Enter Multiple Occurrence Data Points	
• Enter data point • Press 2nd Frq • Enter number of repetitions • Press Σ+ • Repeat for next data points	• Enter "x" data point • Press x:y • Enter "y" data point • Press 2nd Frq • Enter number of repetitions • Press Σ+ • Repeat for next data points
4. To Remove Multiple Occurrence Data Points Entered	
• Press ON/c x:y • Enter unwanted data point • Press 2nd Frq • Enter number of repetitions • Press 2nd Σ−	• Enter unwanted "x" data point • Press x:y • Enter unwanted "y" data point • Press 2nd Frq • Enter number of repetitions • Press 2nd Σ−

The procedures to obtain data are shown in the following chart.

SINGLE-VARIABLE DATA	TWO-VARIABLE DATA
1. Mean	
• Press [2nd] [Mean]	• "y" data points: Press [2nd] [Mean] • "x" data points: Press [2nd] [Mean] [x⇄y]
2. Population Standard Deviation	
• Press [2nd] [σn]	• "y" data points: Press [2nd] [σn] • "x" data points: Press [2nd] [σn] [x⇄y]
3. Sample Standard Deviation	
• Press [2nd] [σn-1]	• "y" data points: Press [2nd] [σn-1] • "x" data points: Press [2nd] [σn-1] [x⇄y]
4. Intercept and Slope	
	• Press [2nd] [b/a] to obtain the intercept • Press [2nd] [b/a] [x⇄y] to obtain the slope
5. One Value Given Another	
	• Enter the x value and press [2nd] [y'] to obtain a "y" value • Enter the y value and press [2nd] [x'] to obtain an "x" value
6. Correlation	
	• Press [2nd] [Corr]

Section 5 — Conversion Keys

Several keys convert units from one system to another and back. Most of the conversions are from the English system of measurement, which most Americans use, to the more convenient metric system used by most of the rest of the world and in scientific and engineering calculations. The final conversions are from the polar expression of points which are graphed to the rectangular system of expression and from degrees/minutes/seconds to degrees and decimal degrees.

[2nd] °F-°C , [INV] [2nd] °F-°C — FAHRENHEIT/CELSIUS CONVERSION KEYS

These keys convert degrees Fahrenheit to degrees Celsius and back. The formulas used are:

$$°C = \frac{5}{9} \times (°F - 32) \qquad °F = \frac{9}{5} \times °C + 32$$

[2nd] gal-l , [INV] [2nd] gal-l — GALLON/LITER CONVERSION KEYS

These keys convert U.S. gallons to liters and back. The formulas used are:

$$l = 3.785411784 \times gal \qquad gal = l \div 3.785411784$$

[2nd] in-cm , [INV] [2nd] in-cm — INCH/CENTIMETER CONVERSION KEYS

These keys convert inches to centimeters and back. The formulas used are:

$$cm = 2.54 \times in \qquad in = cm \div 2.54$$

[2nd] lb-kg , [INV] [2nd] lb-kg — POUND/KILOGRAM CONVERSION KEYS

These keys convert pounds to kilograms and back. The formulas used are:

$$kg = 0.45359237 \times lb \qquad lb = kg \div 0.45359237$$

[2nd] [P↔R], [INV] [2nd] [P↔R] — POLAR/RECTANGULAR CONVERSION KEYS

The rectangular coordinate system describes where points are placed on a grid with a pair of numbers. The first, the x-coordinate, describes the distance of the point from the y-axis, which is a vertical line. The second, the y-coordinate, describes the distance of the point from the x-axis, which is a horizontal line. The following shows the point described in rectangular coordinates as (3,4).

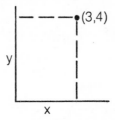

The polar system of coordinates describes a point in terms of a line drawn from a center to the point. It also uses a pair of numbers. The first number is the length of the line, labeled r. The second is the number of degrees the line is from horizontal, labeled theta (θ). The following shows the same point, but described as (5,53.130102°).

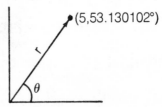

The conversion from polar to rectangular coordinates and back involves some detailed arithmetic. Fortunately, the calculator can perform these calculations.

To convert from polar to rectangular coordinates, follow these steps:

Enter the r value
Press [x:y]
Enter the θ value
Press [2nd] [P↔R]
The y-coordinate is displayed.
Press [x:y]
The x-coordinate is displayed.

To convert from rectangular to polar coordinates, follow these
steps:

Enter the x-coordinate
Press [x:y]
Enter the y-coordinate
Press [INV] [2nd] [P→R]
The θ value is displayed in the units selected by the [DRG] key.
Press [x:y]
The r value is displayed.

The range of θ is from $+180°$ to $-180°$, π to $-\pi$ radians, and 200
to -200 grads.

Note that the [2nd] [P→R] key clears any pending operations.

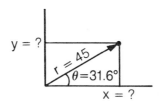

$$y = ?$$
$$r = 45$$
$$\theta = 31.6°$$
$$x = ?$$

Example: Convert r $= 45$ meters, $\theta = 31.6$ degrees to rectangular
coordinates.

Keying it in:

Press	Display	Comments
[ON/C] [ON/C]	0	Clear display and pending operations. Press [DRG] until DEG appears in the display
45 [x:y] 31.6 [2nd] [P→R]	23.579366	y-coordinate value
[x:y]	38.327712	x-coordinate value

[2nd] [DMS-DD], [INV] [2nd] [DMS-DD] — **DEGREES/MINUTES/SECONDS TO DECIMAL DEGREES CONVERSION KEYS**

There are two ways of representing an angle in degrees. One method is to use the decimal degree format DD.dd. Here DD represents the integer portion of the angle and dd represents the fraction portion written as a decimal. Up to 8 digits may be entered.

The second method is to use the degree/minute/second format DD.MMSSss. Again DD represents the whole angle. MM represents minutes and SS denotes seconds. For greater accuracy, fractional seconds may be entered in the ss position. The decimal point separates degrees from minutes.

To convert from the degree/minute/second format to decimal degrees, enter the angle in the display as DD.MMSSss and press [2nd] [DMS-DD]. Pressing [INV] [2nd] [DMS-DD] reverses the conversion process and converts decimal degrees to degrees, minutes, and seconds. Two digits should always be entered for minutes and two for seconds. Trailing zeros need not be entered.

Example: Convert 3°1′30.456″ to decimal degrees and back.

Keying it in:

Press	Display	Comments
[ON/C] [ON/C]	0	Clear display and pending operations. Press [DRG] until DEG appears in the display
3.0130456 [2nd] [DMS-DD]	3.0251267	Answer in decimal degrees
[INV] [2nd] [DMS-DD]	3.0130456	Answer returned to degrees/minutes/seconds

The same process can be used to convert hours, minutes, and seconds to decimal hours and vice versa.

Section 6—Programming Keys

The TI-55-Ⅱ calculator is a powerful problem-solving device, equipped with a variety of features that are ready to use from the keyboard. In addition, the calculator is programmable. This means you can teach the calculator to automatically perform a variety of calculations with up to 56 steps and then have it execute these steps as often as you like with a simple key sequence. In this Section the calculator keys that are devoted to programs and programming are discussed.

The way the calculator learns a program is quite simple. There is a special memory inside called a program memory. It remembers the program keystrokes you press. As you program the calculator, each keystroke sequence is stored, in order, as a simple code. When the program is run, the calculator reads the codes and presses the keys in the exact sequence in which they were pressed.

The memory of the calculator may be visualized as shown in the following diagram.

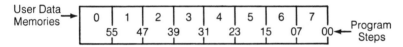

The user data memories are numbered 0 through 7, starting at the left of the diagram. The program steps are numbered 00 through 55, starting at the right of the diagram. Each user data memory takes up the room for eight program steps.

To enter a program, use the programming keys, which are found primarily on the second row of the calculator and connected with a blue band. These keys direct the calculator to accept program keystrokes, alter programs, and run programs.

[2nd] [Part] m — MEMORY PARTITION KEY

WARNING: Before using the [2nd] [Part] m key, remove the engineering and scientific display modes if they are set, and use the [INV] [2nd] [Fix] key to return to standard notation. Leave the statistics mode with [2nd] [CSR] before entering the programming mode.

The [2nd] [Part] key sets the partitioning of the calculator's memory. The space not used for user data memories is available for program steps. The key is followed by the number of user data memories, m, that you wish to have available. The number of program steps and user data memories available is displayed in the format ss.m, where ss is the number of program steps available and m is the number of user data memories available. If you enter [2nd] [Part] followed by 0 or 9, the calculator displays the current partitioning.

The calculator can be set with a maximum of eight user data memories, with no program steps, or a minimum of one user data memory with 56 program steps. When it is set for one through seven user data memories, PROG is shown in the display, indicating that programming steps are available. This indicator is present whether or not there is actually a program in the program steps.

For example, you may set the number of user data memories to three by pressing [2nd] [Part] 3. They are numbered 0, 1, and 2. Enough space is left for 40 program steps, which are numbered 00 through 39.

If you write a program that is too long to fit in the 40 program steps available, but discover that you only need two user data memories, leave the learn mode and repartition the memory to have only two user data memories and 48 program steps. The previously entered 40 steps are not affected. The 8 new program steps, numbers 40 through 47, are added. Any data that was in memory 2 is removed.

If you find that you need only 32 program steps, but need four user data memories, leave the learn mode and repartition the memory to have four user data memories and only 32 program steps. Any program steps in steps 32 through 39 are removed, and memory 3, with 0 in it, is added to the user data memories.

SECTION 6 — PROGRAMMING KEYS

Repartitioning memory only affects the steps or values in the portions of memory that are actually changed from user data memory to program steps or from program steps to user data memory. If the program counter is at a position that becomes user data memory, it is repositioned to step 00.

Certain functions of the calculator make special uses of the memory. Statistical functions require memories 3, 4, 5, 6, and 7. When the statistical mode is entered with [Σ+] or [2nd] [Frq], these memories are cleared. *Any program that you have written is automatically removed when you enter the statistics mode.* When you leave the statistics mode with the [2nd] [CSR] key, partitioning is set to no program steps and eight user data memories and memories 3 through 7 are set to zero.

NOTE: Because the statistical functions use memories 3 through 7, the [2nd] [Part] key is disabled in the statistics mode. For the same reason, none of the statistical keys can be used in a program.

The integration key [∫dx] requires three user data memories, numbers 0, 1, and 2, so a maximum of 40 program steps may be used to enter the function to be integrated.

The Programming Mode Identifier

In the programming mode, the display shows PROG. Set the programming mode by pressing [2nd] [Part] followed by any number 1 through 7. [2nd] [Part] followed by 0 or 9 displays the current partitioning of the calculator. [2nd] [Part] followed by 8 sets eight user data memories, which leaves no programming steps, and leaves the programming mode. Statistics calculations may not be used in the programming mode, so the PROG and STAT indicators cannot be displayed at the same time.

Example: Set the partitioning to 1, 2, 5, and 8 user data memories.

Keying it in: The PROG indicator may or may not be present depending on the current state of the partitioning. If the STAT indicator is present, press 2nd CSR. Remove engineering and scientific notation if necessary. Use the INV 2nd Fix key to return to standard notation.

Press	Display	Comments
ON/C ON/C	0	Clear display and pending operations
2nd Part 1	56.1	Indicates 56 programming steps and one user data memory are available
2nd Part 2	48.2	Indicates 48 programming steps and two user data memories are available
2nd Part 5	24.5	Indicates 24 programming steps and five user data memories are available
2nd Part 8	0.8	Indicates no programming steps and eight user data memories are available. The PROG indicator in the display disappears
2nd Part 9	0.8	Displays the current state of partitioning

PROGRAMMING KEYS

As previously mentioned, the calculator has up to a 56-step program memory, steps 00 through 55. Each step in program memory holds one key function or keystroke. The 2nd key does not use a program step, but is used to identify the second function key that does count as a step. The keys 2nd and INV may be in any order in normal calculations, but must be INV followed by 2nd in a program.

SECTION 6 — PROGRAMMING KEYS

[LRN] — Learn Key

Pressing the [LRN] key once puts the calculator in the learn mode if any programming steps are available. This allows writing a program into program memory to be run later. Pressing [LRN] again takes the calculator out of learn mode and restores the display to its original state.

Once a calculation sequence has been determined, select the learn mode by pressing [LRN] [2nd] **CP** . ([2nd] **CP** removes any previous program and assures that the program is keyed in beginning at location 00.) Then key the sequence into the program memory. The learn mode display has the following format.

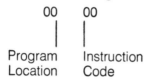

```
00      00
 |       |
Program  Instruction
Location Code
```

Program locations begin at 00 and number consecutively up to the partition. Each location can hold an operation or a single digit. Initially program memory contains zeros in all locations and zeros remain in all locations that are not changed.

An instruction code (or just key code) is a two-digit number assigned to each operation according to its location on the keyboard. Key codes are discussed later. The calculator indicates 00 as the key code when a program is being keyed in because the calculator steps to the next available location as each instruction is keyed in.

Keeping track of the location in the program memory is the function of the program counter. In the learn mode, this counter moves step by step through the program memory up to the partition, displaying the next location to be used. Entering the last step resets the program counter to step 00, takes the calculator out of learn mode, and restores the display to its original state.

[R/S], [RST], [2nd] [Pause] — Run/Stop, Reset, and Pause Keys

The [R/S] key reverses the status of processing. Pressing [R/S] starts program processing at the current position of the program counter. Pressing [R/S] while a program is running stops the program. However, the exact position of the program counter when the program is stopped cannot be predetermined. Entering [R/S] as a program step (while in the learn mode) causes program processing to stop at that point when the program is run.

The [RST] key resets the program counter to step 00, the beginning of the program, and, when used as a program step, also stops the program so that a value can be displayed. [RST] can be used from the keyboard or as a program instruction.

NOTE: If neither [R/S] nor [RST] is present in a program, execution continues up to the partition. Then the program counter is reset to step 00 and execution stops.

The [2nd] [Pause] key, when encountered during program execution, causes the current value of the display register to be displayed for one to two seconds. Pause instructions can be used wherever needed, even consecutively.

[2nd] [CP] — Clear Program Key

Pressing the [2nd] [CP] key while in the learn mode removes the program from program memory and resets the program counter to step 00 so that the calculator is ready for a new program. In any other mode, the [2nd] [CP] key has no effect.

EDITING PROGRAMS

Programs may be changed in several ways. A keystroke input at any point in an existing program, while in the learn mode, writes over the instruction previously stored in that location. As you are singlestepping or back stepping through a program and discover an unwanted instruction, press the correct instruction and it replaces the one that was displayed.

1

[SST], [BST] — Single Step and Backstep Keys

These keys are used in editing a program. While in the learn mode, use these keys to search through the program in order to examine or change it. The [SST] key moves forward one program step. The [BST] key moves back one step. The display shows the program step and the instruction that is in that step. The [SST] key can also be used to execute a program, one step at a time, with the result of each step displayed.

[2nd] **Ins**, [2nd] **Del** — Insert and Delete Keys

In the learn mode, the insert and delete keys allow changing a program by inserting new keystrokes or deleting old ones. To use them, find the proper place in the program using [SST] and [BST]. Then, to insert keystrokes, press [2nd] **Ins** and the keystroke to be inserted. The [2nd] **Ins** key must be repeated for each keystroke to be inserted. The keystrokes that were already in the program are moved to later positions and the instruction in the last available position is lost. To delete keystrokes, press [2nd] **Del** for each keystroke to be deleted. Following key codes are each moved up one position and key code 00 is placed in what was previously the last step. Remember that [2nd] is not a separate keystroke. It is merged with the following instruction.

KEY CODES

The keys are numbered as shown in the following illustration. The first digit of the key code is the number of the row, numbered one through nine. The second digit is the number of the column, numbered 1, 2, 3, 4, and 5. The second function keys are numbered 6, 7, 8, 9, and 0. Thus [ON/c] is 15, [2nd] **Pause** is 20, and [cos] is 33.

The number keys, however, all have a first digit of 0 and a second digit which is equal to the digit. Thus 1 is 01, 2 is 02, 9 is 09, and 0 is 00. The [2nd] key does not have its own code. Instead, it changes the code of the following key. Thus [2nd] **x^2** is listed as 18 rather than 11 followed by 13.

The keys that cannot be used in programming do not have a code.
These include the statistics keys and some of the programming
keys such as [SST] and [2nd] [Part].

TI-55-II Keyboard Showing Key Code and Function Name

		17: [1/x]	18: [x²]		
**: [2nd]	12: [R/S]	13: [√x]		*: [OFF]	15: [ON/c]
*: [Part]	*: [CP]	*: [Ins]		*: [Del]	20: [Pause]
*: [LRN]	22: [RST]	*: [SST]		*: [BST]	*: [∫dx]
		37: [Fix]	38: [°F-°C]	39: [DMS-DD]	30: [DRG▸]
31: [hyp]	32: [sin]	33: [cos]	34: [tan]	35: [DRG]	
		47: [Eng]	48: [gal-l]	49: [lb-kg]	40: [in-cm]
41: [INV]	42: [EE]	43: [log]	44: [lnx]	45: [yˣ]	
*: [Σ−]	57: [P→R]	58: [%]	59: [Δ%]	*: [Corr]	
*: [Σ+]	52: [x:y]	53: [(]	54: [)]	55: [÷]	
*: [Mean]	67: [x!]	68: [nPr]	69: [nCr]	*: [b/a]	
61: [STO]	07: [7]	08: [8]	09: [9]	65: [X]	
*: [σn-1]	77: [Sgn]	78: [Frac]	79: [K]	*: [x']	
71: [RCL]	04: [4]	05: [5]	06: [6]	75: [−]	
*: [σn]	87: [|x|]	88: [Intg]	89: [CM]	*: [y']	
81: [EXC]	01: [1]	02: [2]	03: [3]	85: [+]	
*: [Frq]				*: [CSR]	
91: [π]	00: [0]	93: [·]	94: [+/−]	95: [=]	

*: No key code. These keys cannot be put in programs.
**: This key is merged with the following key stroke.

Key Codes in Numeric Order

00: [0]	22: [RST]	47: [2nd] [Eng]	75: [−]
01: [1]	30: [2nd] [DRG▸]	48: [2nd] [gal-l]	77: [2nd] [Sgn]
02: [2]	31: [hyp]	49: [2nd] [lb-kg]	78: [2nd] [Frac]
03: [3]	32: [sin]	52: [x⇄y]	79: [2nd] [K]
04: [4]	33: [cos]	53: [(]	81: [EXC]
05: [5]	34: [tan]	54: [)]	85: [+]
06: [6]	35: [DRG]	55: [÷]	87: [2nd] [|x|]
07: [7]	37: [2nd] [Fix]	57: [2nd] [P↔R]	88: [2nd] [Intg]
08: [8]	38: [2nd] [°F-°C]	58: [2nd] [%]	89: [2nd] [CM]
09: [9]	39: [2nd] [DMS-DD]	59: [2nd] [Δ%]	91: [π]
12: [R/S]	40: [2nd] [in-cm]	61: [STO]	93: [.]
13: [√x]	41: [INV]	65: [×]	94: [+/−]
15: [ON/c]	42: [EE]	67: [2nd] [x!]	95: [=]
17: [2nd] [1/x]	43: [log]	68: [2nd] [nPr]	
18: [2nd] [x²]	44: [lnx]	69: [2nd] [nCr]	
20: [2nd] [Pause]	45: [yˣ]	71: [RCL]	

PROGRAMMING EXAMPLES

Suppose you have received a sale notice from a department store indicating that all the items listed in their current catalog will be marked down 15% for one day only. There are several items that you are interested in buying, so you use your calculator to find the new price: Price [−] 15 [2nd] [%] [=]. To check the sale price of 25 different items, you have to press this key sequence 25 times. However, calculations that have to be done repeatedly are easy using the programming feature of the TI-55-II. The program has to be entered only once. Then enter the price of each item, start the program, and the calculator presses the keys in the program.

Keying it in: First set the number of user 'data memories that you expect to use. This program will probably use no user data memory locations. However, there is always one user data memory (number 0) available. This leaves 56 programming steps, but you probably will not use them all. The [2nd] [Part] key sets the partitioning of the calculator.

Press the [LRN] key to enter the learn mode. Press [2nd] [CP] to clear any previous program and reset to step 00. The display changes to a unique format that indicates that the calculator is ready to learn and remember the keystrokes.

00   00

The left two digits show the program step number (from 00 to 55) and the right two show the key codes.

After entering the learn mode, press the keys needed to solve the problem. Leave the learn mode by pressing [LRN] again.

Press	Display		Comments
[ON/c] [ON/c] [2nd] [CSR]		0	Clear display, pending operations, and statistical registers
[2nd] [Part] 1		56.1	Select 56 programming steps and 1 user data memory
[LRN] [2nd] [CP]	00	00	Enter the learn mode and clear the program memory
[−] 15 [2nd] [%] [=]	05	00	Take the displayed value (entered separately for each problem) and subtract the 15% discount from it

Note that the program counter has advanced to 05 showing that steps 00 through 04 have been used for the program.

SECTION 6—PROGRAMMING KEYS

At this point one more action is required. The calculator has the answer, but it needs to stop and show the result. This is accomplished with the [R/S] key.

Press	Display	Comments
[R/S]	06 00	Tells the program to stop and display the results

When the program is finished, leave the learn mode. Pressing [LRN] again does this.

Press	Display	Comments
[LRN]	56.1	The display is restored

Before running the program, the [RST] key must be used to put the program counter back to step 00, the start of the program. Each time the program is run you must start it at the beginning, step 00, with [RST].

Find the reduced prices on items discounted 15% at an original cost of $9.95, $12.95, and $49.95. While working with money, fix the decimal at two places.

Press	Display	Comments
[ON/C] [ON/C] [2nd] **Fix** 2	0.00	Clear display and pending operations and fix decimal at two places
[RST]	0.00	Reset to step 00
9.95 [R/S]	8.46	9.95 − 15% = 8.46
12.95 [RST]	12.95	Enter new price and reset to step 00
[R/S]	11.01	New discount price
49.95 [RST]	49.95	Enter price and reset
[R/S]	42.46	Discount price

This problem can be done repeatedly by entering the price to be discounted, resetting the program, and starting it.

Using [RST] as a Program Step

The above example shows that programming can save many steps with repetitive calculations. The discount program can be improved, however, by replacing [R/S] with [RST]. Then each time you work a problem the program comes to the [RST], goes back to step 00, stops, and displays the discounted price. When a new price is entered and [R/S] is pressed, the program repeats and calculates the next discount price. Thus reset does not have to be pressed each time.

Keying it in: The program can be changed by finding the [R/S] key (key code 12) at step 05 and replacing it with the [RST] key.

Press	Display		Comments
[RST]		42.46	Reset to step 00
[LRN]	00	75	Enter the learn mode
[SST] [SST] [SST] [SST] [SST]	05	12	Use singlestep to find the [R/S]
[RST]	06	00	Change it to a [RST]
[LRN] [RST]		****	Leave learn mode and reset for the first calculation. The display is restored to whatever it was before the learn mode was entered.

To try the program, find the discount price for $14.95, $7.50, and $24.75.

Press	Display	Comments
[ON/C] [ON/C] [2nd] **Fix** 2	0.00	Clear display and pending operations and fix decimal at two places
14.95 [R/S]	12.71	
7.5 [R/S]	6.38	
24.75 [R/S]	21.04	

SECTION 6—PROGRAMMING KEYS

Using Insert and Delete

Example: Suppose you need a program that solves the equation $y=2x^2+4x$. The entry of it, and the resulting key codes, are shown below.

Keying it in:

Press	Display		Comments
[ON/C] [ON/C] [INV] [2nd] **Fix**		0	Clear display and pending operations and return to standard notation
[2nd] **Part** 2		48.2	Set partitioning to 48 programming steps and two user data memories
[LRN] [2nd] **CP**	00	00	Enter learn mode and clear program
[STO] 0	02	00	Store the number in the display in user data memory 0
[2nd] **x^2** [X] 2	05	00	Square number and multiply by 2
[+] 4 [X] [RCL] 0	10	00	Add 4 times number in memory 0
[=] [RST]	12	00	Finish pending operations, reset to step 00, and display result

The resulting program looks like this:

Step	Key Code	Description	Comments
00	61	STO	Store the number in the display
01	00	0	User data memory in which to store the number
02	18	2nd x^2	Square the number in the display
03	65	X	Multiply the square
04	02	2	Number by which to multiply
05	85	+	Addition instruction
06	04	4	Beginning of what to add
07	65	X	Multiply instruction
08	71	RCL	Recall number from memory
09	00	0	Which memory
10	95	=	Finish pending operations
11	22	RST	Reset to step 00 and display result

After entering this program, leave the learn mode with LRN and return to step 00 with RST.

Press	Display	Comments
LRN RST	****	The display is restored to whatever it was before the learn mode was entered

Then run the program with values for x such as 7 and 4.

Press	Display	Comments
7 R/S	126	Value of "y" when "x" is 7
4 R/S	48	Value of "y" when "x" is 4

Suppose you need to change this program. You now need to evaluate the equation $y=2x^2-4x+7$. At first you may want to key in a new program, but in many cases it is easier to change the program you already have. All you need to do is change the +4x to a −4x (the plus to a minus), and add the +7 at the end.

You can change any program step to a new one simply by going to that step, in the learn mode, and keying the new step over the old one. The [+] is at step 05 (key code 85). Press [RST] and then follow these steps.

Press	Display		Comments
[LRN]	00	61	First program step
[SST]	01	00	
[SST]	02	18	
[SST]	03	65	
[SST]	04	02	
[SST]	05	85	Step to be changed
[−]	06	04	New step is put over the old one. The display shows the next step
[BST]	05	75	New code at step 05. Plus has been changed to minus

Now add +7 to the end of the original program. The key code for the [=] key is 95, and is at step 10 in the original program. You need to insert a +7 at that point. So step to 10 with the [SST] key.

Press	Display		Comments
[SST]	06	04	
[SST]	07	65	
[SST]	08	71	
[SST]	09	00	
[SST]	10	95	

Now use the insert key.

Press	Display		Comments
2nd Ins	10	00	The display shows that step 10 is now clear, ready to have a new step inserted
+	11	95	Display moves to the next step. Note the 95 key code. The = has been moved to step 11
2nd Ins	11	00	Step 11 is now clear
7	12	95	Again the display moves to the next step. = has been moved to step 12 and the 7 has been inserted at step 11
BST	11	07	7 at step 11
BST	10	85	+ at step 10. All changes have been made correctly
LRN RST		****	The display is restored. Reset to step 00

Now run the program and get the new values of y.

Press	Display	Comments
7 R/S	77	Value of y when x is 7
4 R/S	23	Value of y when x is 4

SECTION 6—PROGRAMMING KEYS

As an example of the delete key, suppose you need to change the program back to evaluating $y=2x^2+4x$. To do this, change the minus back to plus and delete the +7.

Press	Display		Comments
[LRN]	00	61	
[SST]	01	00	
[SST]	02	18	
[SST]	03	65	
[SST]	04	02	
[SST]	05	75	This is the code for [−], which you wish to change back to [+]
[+]	06	04	
[BST]	05	85	Go back and check, then go on
[SST]	06	04	
[SST]	07	65	
[SST]	08	71	
[SST]	09	00	
[SST]	10	85	[+] key at step 10. Delete the next two steps
[2nd] Del	10	07	
[2nd] Del	10	95	Now the 95 code [=] is where it belongs and +7 has been deleted

At this point you have completed the changes to the program, so press [LRN] and [RST]. The program is ready to use.

Section 7 — Integration

Definite integrals can be calculated using Simpson's Rule, which is described in the Appendix. An integral can be thought of as the area under a curve. The calculator finds the approximate areas under portions of the curve and sums them. The more portions under the curve, the more accurate the answer, but the more time it takes.

$\boxed{\text{∫dx}}$ — INTEGRATION KEY

The $\boxed{\text{∫dx}}$ key is used in conjunction with a program to find the definite integral of a function. The following are the steps to follow in finding a definite integral.

- Partition with at least three user data memories. $\boxed{\text{∫dx}}$ *is only operative in program mode with at least three user data memories.* "Error" is displayed if there are fewer than three user data memories.

- Put the function to be integrated in program memory, followed by $\boxed{=}$ and ended with $\boxed{\text{R/S}}$, $\boxed{\text{RST}}$, or the partition. *User data memories 0, 1, and 2 should not be changed by the function.* The integration argument is automatically recalled from user data memory 1 at the beginning of each integration interval. Otherwise, it must be recalled from user data memory 1 whenever it is needed.

- Leave the learn mode and enter the lower limit in user data memory 1 and the upper limit in user data memory 2.

- Press $\boxed{\text{∫dx}}$ and the calculator prompts for the number of integration intervals you wish. You may enter any number up to 99. The more divisions, the more accurate the answer is. However, the more divisions, the longer the integration takes.

- Press $\boxed{\text{R/S}}$.

The integral is figured according to Simpson's Rule, which is described in the Appendix. At the end of the integration, the integral is displayed and placed in user data memory 0, and user data memories 1 and 2 both contain the upper limit.

Most trigonometric integral tables assume that the angular measure used is radians. Therefore, to get the answers that those tables give, your calculator should be in RAD mode and you should use radians. If you use degrees or grads on a function that contains only trigonometric functions, you can convert the answer to radians by converting the display to the RAD mode. For exam-

ple, the integral of (sin x)dx evaluated in degrees with 40 intervals between 0° and 180° is 114.59156. This is equal to

$$- (\cos x)\frac{dx}{d\theta} \Big|_{0°}^{180°} \text{, where } \frac{dx}{d\theta} \text{ is equal to } \frac{180}{\pi}.$$

Converting to radians gives 2, which is the answer if the integral were done between 0 and π radians. There is no simple way to convert the answer to the integral of a function such as (sin x + x)dx that contains both trigonometric and nontrigonometric functions, so for integrals of that type you must select the proper angular mode.

Some functions have inverse trigonometric functions as their integrals. For such a function the answer is given in radians regardless of the calculator's mode. For example, the integral of $(1/(\sqrt{2x-x^2}))dx$ is $\cos^{-1}(1-x)$ and the result when evaluated with 10 intervals between 1 and 1.5 is 0.5235988 radians. See the example on page **6**-18.

Example: Suppose you wish to integrate sin x cos x between 0 and $\pi \div 4$ radians.

Keying it in: First press $\boxed{\text{DRG}}$ until RAD is in the display.

Press	Display		Comments
$\boxed{\text{ON/C}}$ $\boxed{\text{ON/C}}$ $\boxed{\text{2nd}}$ $\boxed{\text{Part}}$ 3	40.3		Clear display and pending operations and set 40 programming steps and 3 user data memories.
$\boxed{\text{LRN}}$ $\boxed{\text{2nd}}$ $\boxed{\text{CP}}$	00	00	Enter learn mode and clear the program memory
$\boxed{\text{RCL}}$ 1	02	00	Recall value in user data memory 1
$\boxed{\text{sin}}$	03	00	Find the sine
$\boxed{\text{X}}$	04	00	Multiply
$\boxed{\text{RCL}}$ 1	06	00	Recall value in user data memory 1

(continued)

(continued)

Press	Display		Comments
[cos]	07	00	Find the cosine
[=]	08	00	Complete the operation
[R/S]	09	00	Stop and display the answer.
[LRN] [RST]		40.3	Leave the learn mode and reset to step 00
0 [STO] 1		0	Store the lower limit in user data memory 1
[π] [÷] 4 [=] [STO] 2		0.7853982	Store the upper limit in user data memory 2
[∫dx]		Int 00	Asks for interval to be used
20		Int 20	Set the interval to be used
[R/S]		0.25	The answer

While the integral is being figured, the indicators are displayed and the digits disappear, except that the display briefly shows the value of the function at the end of each integration interval. You can time this program. Typically it takes between two and three minutes to do.

Steps 00 and 01 ([RCL] 1) are not necessary because there is an automatic [RCL] 1 at the beginning of each iteration of the integration. The displayed value is ignored. There are two advantages to removing these steps. First, you save two steps which might be needed for other keystrokes. Second, the program runs more quickly.

Remove steps 00 and 01 (using [RST], [LRN], and [2nd] [Del]). Then leave the learn mode, put the upper limit in user data memory 2, and the lower limit in user data memory 1. Do the integration again with the [∫dx] 20 [R/S] key sequence. Now the problem takes typically six to seven percent less time than when the first two steps were included.

If fewer intervals are used, the problem is solved more quickly, but the answer varies slightly. This variation may be acceptable for your uses.

Elementary Programming

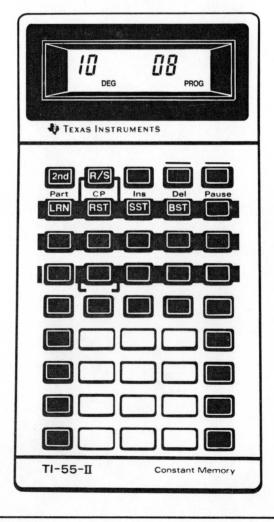

The ability to program is an added benefit of the TI-55-II. It allows placing a series of keystrokes in the program memory and having those keystrokes executed, quickly and accurately, as many times as needed.

Programming on the TI-55-II is as simple as entering the keystrokes. Work through the problem yourself, and then enter the keystrokes while in the learn mode. Once entered, a program may be run as often as needed. It is the ability to run a program repeatedly, with different data, that makes programming useful.

This chapter assumes that you have read the descriptions and worked the examples shown in Section 6, Programming Keys, in Chapter 1.

Area of a Circle

A program can be quite simple. The first example determines the area of a circle given its radius.

Target: Given any radius, find the area of a circle.

Tools: The formula for the area of a circle is $A = \pi r^2$. The easiest way to supply the radius is to put it in the display before running the program. An alternative is to put it into a memory. Each of these methods is shown.

Keying it in: This program assumes that the radius is in the display when it starts executing. It takes the number in the display, squares it, multiplies the result by π, resets to step 00 (to prepare for the next run), stops, and displays the result.

Press	Display	Comments
[ON/C] [ON/C] [2nd] **CSR**	0	Clear display and pending operations and be sure the statistics mode is cleared
[INV] [2nd] **Eng**		
[INV] [2nd] **Fix**	0	Be sure that the calculator is in standard display format
[2nd] **Part** 5	24.5	Set partitioning to 24 program steps and 5 user data memories
[LRN] [2nd] **.CP**	00 00	Enter learn mode and clear any previous program
[2nd] x^2	01 00	Squares the value in the display (the radius)
[X] [π] [=]	04 00	Multiplies the result by π
[RST]	05 00	Resets to step 00, stops, and displays the result
[LRN] [RST]	24.5	Leave learn mode and reset to step 00. The display is restored to the value it held when the [LRN] key was pressed

The program is complete. Find the areas of circles with radii of 2, 7, and 4567.

Press	Display	Comments
2 [R/S]	12.566371	The area with a radius of 2
7 [R/S]	153.93804	The area with a radius of 7
4567 [R/S]	65525734	The area with a radius of 4567

That is the best method to program the solution for this problem. Often, however, it is more useful to store values in a memory for use by the program. For demonstration purposes, putting the radius in a memory is shown.

Keying it in: The following program assumes that the radius is in memory 0. It takes π times the square of the number in memory 0, resets to step 00, stops, and displays the result.

Press	Display	Comments
[ON/C] [ON/C]	0	Clear display and pending operations
[LRN] [2nd] **CP**	00 00	Enter learn mode and clear any previous program
[π] [X]	02 00	Start multiplying by π
[RCL] 0	04 00	Recall radius from memory 0
[2nd] **x²**	05 00	Square the radius
[=] [RST]	07 00	Finish the problem, reset to step 00, stop, and display the result
[LRN] [RST]	****	Leave learn mode and reset to step 00. The display is restored

Find the area of circles with radii of 8 and 142.6

Press	Display	Comments
8 [STO] 0	8	Store the radius in memory 0
[R/S]	201.06193	The area with a radius of 8
142.6 [STO] 0 [R/S]	63883.533	The area with a radius of 142.6

Projectile Calculations

The best type of problem to program is one which can be used repeatedly with different data.

Target: Given the original velocity and angle from the horizontal of a projectile, determine the time that it spends in the air before it lands, its maximum height, and the distance from its launch point when it lands. Assume that there is no air resistance.

The following shows the situation.

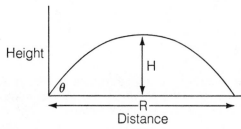

Tools:

The formulas are as follows:

$$T = \frac{\sin\theta \times 2 \times v}{g}$$

$$H = \frac{(\sin\theta \times v)^2}{2 \times g}$$

$$R = \frac{\sin 2\theta \times v^2}{g}$$

where

T is the time (in seconds),
H is the maximum height (in meters),
R is the distance traveled (in meters),
θ is the angle at which the projectile starts (which may be in degrees, radians, or grads).
v is the starting velocity (in meters per second), and
g is the gravitational constant (9.81 meters per second squared).

Note that if the starting velocity and gravitational constant are given in some other units, then the maximum height and distance traveled will be in that other unit.

PROJECTILE CALCULATIONS

Keying it in: Store the values for θ and v in memories 0 and 1. Then the three problems can be worked, with the calculator stopping to display the result after each calculation.

Press	Display	Comments
ON/c ON/c	0	Clear display and pending operations
2nd Part 2	48.2	Set partitioning to 48 programming steps and 2 memories
LRN 2nd CP	00 00	Enter learn mode and clear the previous program
RCL 0 sin	03 00	Take the sine of θ
X 2 X RCL 1	08 00	Multiply by 2 and by the velocity
÷ 9.81 = R/S	15 00	Divide by the gravitational constant, stop, and display the time in seconds
RCL 0 sin X		
RCL 1 =	22 00	Find the sine of θ and multiply by the velocity
2nd x^2 ÷ 2 ÷ 9.81	30 00	Square the numerator and divide the result by twice the gravitational constant
= R/S	32 00	Finish the problem, stop, and display the maximum height
2 X RCL 0 =	37 00	Take 2 times θ
sin X RCL 1 2nd x^2	42 00	Take the sine and multiply by the square of the velocity

(continued)

(continued)

Press	Display	Comments
÷ 9.81	47 00	Divide by the gravitational constant
=	48.2	Finish the problem. The partition has been reached, so the calculator automatically resets to step 00, stops, and displays the distance traveled. The calculator leaves the learn mode and resets to step 00 because all 48 available programming steps have been entered

Find the time that a projectile spends in the air before it lands, its maximum height, and the distance from its launch point when it lands if θ is 45° and the starting velocity is 20 meters per second.

Press DRG until DEG is displayed.

Press	Display	Comments
ON/C ON/C	0	Clear display and pending operations
45 STO 0	45	Store θ in memory 0
20 STO 1	20	Store the starting velocity in memory 1
R/S	2.8832081	The time is 2.88 seconds
R/S	10.19368	The maximum height reached is 10.2 meters
R/S	40.77472	The distance traveled from the starting point is 40.8 meters

If the velocity is given in different units, then the program must be changed slightly.

Find the time that a projectile spends in the air before it lands, its maximum height, and the distance from its launch point when it lands if θ is 1.2 radians and the starting velocity is 500 feet per second.

Keying it in: The gravitational constant must be changed from 9.81 meters per second squared to 32.2 feet per second squared. This can be done by keying the new number over the old at steps 9 through 12, 27 through 30, and 43 through 46.

Press DRG until RAD is shown in the display.

Press	Display		Comments
ON/c ON/c		0	Clear display and pending operations
LRN	00	71	Enter learn mode
SST SST SST SST SST	05	65	Single step to step 09
SST SST SST SST	09	09	
32.2	13	95	Replace metric gravitational constant with English equivalent
SST SST SST SST SST	18	65	Single step to step 26
SST SST SST SST SST	23	55	
SST SST SST	26	09	
32.2	30	95	Replace metric gravitational constant with English equivalent
SST SST SST SST SST	35	00	Single step to step 43
SST SST SST SST SST	40	01	
SST SST SST	43	09	
32.2	47	95	Replace metric gravitational constant with English equivalent
LRN RST		****	Leave learn mode and reset to step 00. The display is restored

Now enter the data and run the problem.

Press	Display	Comments
1.2 [STO] 0	1.2	Store θ in memory 0
500 [STO] 1	500	Store the starting velocity in memory 1
[R/S]	28.945313	The time is 28.95 seconds
[R/S]	3372.2704	The maximum height reached is 3372.3 feet
[R/S]	5244.2794	The distance traveled from the starting point is 5244.3 feet

Measuring & Forecasting Trends

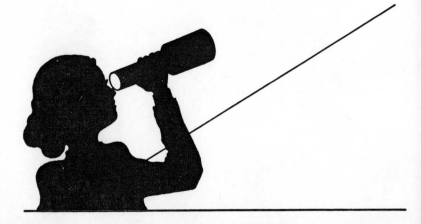

Knowledge about and some control over what will happen in the future is an important aspect of managing any type of business. The more you can predict about how prices will vary, how well a sales force will perform, how advertising will affect sales, etc., the easier it is to make sound decisions in a variety of business situations. Knowing how well one variable relates to another can allow you to make better decisions in your everyday life, as well as in your business.

The following examples illustrate some techniques that can be used to make predictions of future performance based on past records. Tools for making decisions about whether or not two variables are related and how much you can rely on the relationship are also discussed. Your calculator is equipped with special keys that make handling the mathematics involved simple. These keys perform the very useful mathematical tools that statisticians call the techniques of linear regression and correlation.

Linear Regression

The linear regression function of the calculator uses the ⟨x:y⟩ and ⟨Σ+⟩ keys, as well as the second function keys labeled **Frq**, **Corr**, **b/a**, **x'**, and **y'**.

In linear regression the calculator mathematically draws the best fitting line through a series of data points. To enable it to do this, key in the data with the ⟨x:y⟩, ⟨Σ+⟩, and ⟨2nd⟩ **Frq** keys. The basic elements of how these keys are used were discussed in Chapter 1. In this chapter the processes are reviewed in more detail. The techniques described in this chapter allow you to make predictions on any process or operation that can be assumed to follow a straight line pattern of behavior.

Example: Suppose you have data about some type of process or operation, and need to make predictions based on this data. Data such as this is often expressed in terms of pairs of numbers labeled with the letters "x" and "y", such as those tabulated below. The points could be plotted as shown:

x	y	
1.5	2.25	
3.0	3.0	Five data
4.25	5.5	points you
6.0	3.5	know
8.0	7.0	
12	?	Predictions you
?	11.25	need to make.

The values of "x" and "y" can be any of a variety of variables with some relationship between them such as thousands of dollars of advertising vs. sales volume in hundreds of units, employees' scores on an exam vs. performance, etc. The task is to make predictions based on the data. Typical things you might need to know in this case could be:

For a given "x" value (say x = 12), what is the value of "y"? or For what "x" value will "y" reach some specific number (say 11.25)?

You might also like to know how accurate the predictions are, as well as how to make additional predictions at a later time.

NOTE: Caution should be used in computing an "x" (independent) value on the basis of a "y" (dependent) value. Further, it is not valid to compute a "y" value on the basis of an "x" which is outside the range of the entered "x" values. The predictions which result do not have statistical validity, and the probability figures that are found are not valid. However, trend line analysis and forecasting calculations often use these computations to make predictions or estimations of probability about the future. When performing such calculations, the actual values may differ from the calculated values.

Keying it in: If STAT is displayed, press [2nd] [CSR]. Then enter the information (the data) as follows: enter each "x" value, press [x:y], enter the corresponding "y" value, then press [Σ+]. Repeat the process for all the data.

For the data tabulated in the example:

Press	Display	Comments
[ON/C] [ON/C] [2nd] [CSR]	0	Clear display, pending operations, and statistical registers
1.5 [x:y] 2.25 [Σ+]	1	Also displayed are STAT and DEG after pressing [Σ+]
3 [x:y] 3 [Σ+]	2	Notice that the calculator
4.25 [x:y] 5.5 [Σ+]	3	keeps track of how many
6 [x:y] 3.5 [Σ+]	4	data points (pairs of "x"
8 [x:y] 7 [Σ+]	5	and "y" values) are entered

To predict a "y" value for a given "x" value, enter the "x" value, and press [2nd] **y'**.

Press	Display	Comments
12 [2nd] **y'**	8.8882025	The "y" value when "x" = 12

There is a slight pause when you press the **y'** key before the result is displayed. That is because the calculator is working through the linear regression calculation. Here is the formula.

$$y' = \left[\frac{\dfrac{\Sigma x_i\, \Sigma y_i}{N} - \Sigma x_i y_i}{\dfrac{(\Sigma x_i)^2}{N} - \Sigma x_i^2} \right] \times \text{(your "x" value)}$$

$$+ \left\{ \frac{\Sigma y_i}{N} - \left[\frac{\dfrac{\Sigma x_i\, \Sigma y_i}{N} - \Sigma x_i y_i}{\dfrac{(\Sigma x_i)^2}{N} - \Sigma x_i^2} \right] \left(\frac{\Sigma x_i}{N} \right) \right\}$$

To find an "x" value for a given "y" value, enter the "y" value, then press [2nd] **x'**.

Press	Display	Comments
11.25 [2nd] **x'**	15.79358	The "x" value for "y" = 11.25

The Correlation Coefficient

The ⟨2nd⟩ ⟨Corr⟩ key sequence displays the linear correlation coefficient of the two sets of data ("x"s and "y"s). A value close to positive 1 indicates a high positive relationship and a value close to minus 1 indicates a high negative relationship. As the value gets closer to zero the two sets of data become less related. Note that it is possible that "x" and "y" might have a nonlinear relationship even if the linear correlation coefficient is near zero. This chapter, however, discusses only linear relationships.

To find out how well the data correlates press ⟨2nd⟩ ⟨Corr⟩. The correlation coefficient for the line is then displayed. For the example:

Press	Display	Comments
⟨2nd⟩ ⟨Corr⟩	0.8097825	Correlation coefficient

Caution: Cause and Effect

Be careful about drawing conclusions about cause and effect. Two variables that are related to a third can show a relationship to each other without a "cause and effect" relationship between them.

For example, you may have data on children that relates manual dexterity (the time to finish a jigsaw puzzle) to mathematical ability (performance on a math test). There may be a high correlation coefficient. Further analysis may show, however, that the older children display both better manual coordination and mathematical skill and that if the sample is restructured to include only children of the same age an entirely different relationship may result. So be careful about applying results in making decisions. Consider the makeup of the sample and exactly what is being measured and tested.

Slope and Intercept

To find out more about the line, press [2nd] [b/a] and [x:y] to display
the intercept and slope of the line.

Press	Display	Comments
[2nd] [b/a]	1.4172723	Intercept
[x:y]	0.6225775	Slope

The slope of the line is the ratio of its "rise" to its "run," while the intercept is the point where the line crosses the y axis. Any straight
line may be expressed as an equation written in the form:

$y = ax + b$
where a is the slope value and b is the intercept value.

Using the calculated values, write an equation for the line best fitting the data as follows:

$y = (.62)x + 1.42$ (The slope and intercept have been
rounded.)

This equation can now be used to predict a "y" value for any selected "x" value with a simple calculation at some future time, without
reentering all the data.

Summary

The following diagram illustrates all of the information discussed so far.

After entering the x,y coordinates of the known values

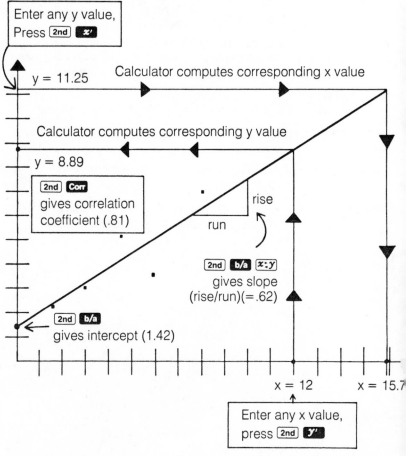

The rest of the chapter gives a few examples of how these procedures can be used.

Predicting Sales from Advertising (Linear Regression)

Suppose a company recently started advertising in a new medium (say a series of magazines), on a weekly basis. The marketing manager has a record of the amount spent on advertising each week ("x") and the corresponding sales volume ("y"). The question is: What is the expected sales volume if $3250 is spent on magazine advertising next week?

Amount Spent on Advertising ("x")	Weekly Sales Volume ("y")
$1000	101,000
$1250	126,000
$1500	163,000
$2000	194,000
$2500	209,000
$3250	?

Target: Predict what will happen, in unit sales ("y"), if the advertising budget ("x") is increased to $3250, using the best straight line approximation.

Tools: You will be using the linear regression feature of the calculator to help predict the result. First, enter the information:

Enter $ in advertising:
 press [x:y]
Enter corresponding unit sales:
 press [Σ+]

To make the prediction, enter the trial advertising dollar value and press [2nd] [y'] .

NOTE: As you get further outside the range of the known "x" values, the reliability of the corresponding "y" value decreases.

To find out how well the data correlates to the straight line drawn through the data points, press [2nd] [Corr] to display the correlation coefficient. A value near 1 means a fairly good linear correlation.

Keying it in: First, enter the data:

Press	Display	Comments
[ON/C] [ON/C] [2nd] [CSR]	0	Clear display, pending operations, and statistics registers

Enter the 5 data points:

	Display	Comments
1000 [x:y] 101000 [Σ+]	1	
1250 [x:y] 126000 [Σ+]	2	The calculator displays the
1500 [x:y] 163000 [Σ+]	3	number of (x,y) points that
2000 [x:y] 194000 [Σ+]	4	have been entered
2500 [x:y] 209000 [Σ+]	5	

Now find the "y" value for "x" = $3250

	Display
3250 [2nd] [y']	274517.24

Based on the best straight line approximation, the projected weekly sales volume for $3250 spent on advertising is approximately 274,500 units. This is assuming there is no change in the relationship of "x" to "y" over time.

Now to see how good an estimate the calculator has made:

Press	Display	Comments
[2nd] [Corr]	0.9637964	

The correlation is good, but the small number of points used and the distance that 3250 is outside the other "x" values make this less significant.

Decision time: You are now in a position to make predictions about future sales based on advertising. The correlation coefficient seems to indicate that the prediction will be a good one, but re-

member the total number of data points is small. There are only 5 points upon which to predict the future. There is a way to further analyze the correlation that allows you to take the number of data points into account (see the Correlation Coefficient Significance Section).

To make a decision at this point, take a look at the increased cost and weigh that against the increase in sales that you predict will result.

Press	Display	Comments
ON/c ON/c	0	Clear display and pending operations
3250 − 2500 =	750	Amount of advertising increase
274517.24 − 209000 =	65517.24	Increase in unit sales predicted.

Correlation Coefficient Significance

As previously mentioned, in this example you are predicting the future based on only five data points from the past. That is not much to go on. In general, the less data you have to go on, the less reliable the prediction. You want to know if there is a significant possibility that such a large value as this correlation coefficient could be due to chance alone. There is a quick way to get a measure of how significant the correlation coefficient is under different data conditions. (As a general rule, if there is not much data, unless the correlation coefficient is quite close to plus or minus one, you cannot be too sure of it).

One procedure for a quick check on the significance of the correlation coefficient is as follows:

a) Decide on how sure you would like (or need) the correlation coefficient to be, say 95%.

b) Locate the r_{test} (test correlation coefficient) value from the table at the end of this chapter for the degree of certainty selected and the number of samples used.

c) If the calculated correlation coefficient is greater than the r_{test} value, you can be certain (to the degree selected) that the calculated correlation coefficient was not due to chance alone.

For the previous example, the calculated correlation coefficient is 0.96. Compare this to the r_{test} value; at 95% certainty for 5 samples (find this value in the tables):

$$r_{test} = .878$$

Since the correlation coefficient is greater than r_{test}, it is correct to assume that the correlation coefficient is not due to chance alone with a 95% degree of certainty. (Being 95% certain of a conclusion means that 95 times out of 100 you will be correct).

NOTE: Since the "x" value used for prediction (3250) is outside the range of "x" values entered, this degree of certainty is not statistically accurate. It is, however, an indication of the certainty.

Earnings Per Share Projections (Trend Line Analysis)

In many instances data is collected in the form of a series of yearly figures, and you need to predict what will happen in subsequent years. This type of prediction involves what statisticians call trend line analysis. Trend line analysis is a special type of linear regression. The calculator has features that make trend line analysis easy.

Example: A stock has reported the following earnings per share during the past few years:

> $1.52 in 1976
> $1.35 in 1977
> $1.53 in 1978
> $2.17 in 1979
> $3.60 in 1980

You would like to predict the earnings per share for the next three years. You would also like to know in what year you could expect the earnings per share to reach $6.50.

Target: You wish to enter the data you have into the calculator, and then use trend line analysis to make predictions. You would also like to know how well the two sets of data correlate.

 Tools: First, enter the data, using the ⌨x:y and ⌨Σ+ keys. In this case the "x" values are a series of years in sequence, and the "y" values are the earnings per share recorded for each year. (Data for a series of successive years is common in trend line analysis situations.)

In trend line analysis, the calculator automatically adds 1 to the "x" variable.

> Enter the first "x" value (the first year, 1976) and press ⌨x:y, then enter a "y" value ($1.52 earnings per share) and press ⌨Σ+. The first data point is entered.

Then:

> Enter the second data point by just entering the "y" value (for this example $1.35) and pressing ⌨Σ+. The calculator automatically increments the "x" variable by 1.

After the data is entered:

To make predictions on earnings for future years:
Enter the year and press [2nd] [y']

To predict in what year a certain level of earnings per share will be reached:
Enter the earnings and press [2nd] [x']

To see how well the two sets of data correlate:
Press [2nd] [Corr]

Keying it in:

Press	Display	Comments
[ON/c] [ON/c] [2nd] [CSR]	0	Clear display, pending operations, and statistical registers
[2nd] [Fix] 2	0.00	This sets the display to show only two decimal places.

Now enter the data:

1976 [x:y] 1.52 [Σ+]	1.00	Note: the calculator
1.35 [Σ+]	2.00	increases the "x" value by 1
1.53 [Σ+]	3.00	automatically unless another
2.17 [Σ+]	4.00	value is entered
3.6 [Σ+]	5.00	

Decision Time: To predict the earnings for future years (future "y" values) key in the year, and press [2nd] [y']:

Press	Display	Comments
1981 [2nd] [y']	3.53	Earnings of $3.53 per share are projected for 1981
1982 [2nd] [y']	4.03	For 1982
1983 [2nd] [y']	4.52	For 1983

You can now make decisions based on the pattern of growth you are watching or predict when the earnings per share will reach a specified value. For example, to calculate when the earnings will reach $6.50 (if the earning trend continues), enter 6.5 and press
[2nd] **x'**

Press | **Display** | **Comments**
6.5 [2nd] **x'** | 1986.97 | About 1987

Going further: To see how well the two sets of data are correlated just press [2nd] **Corr** .

Press | **Display** | **Comments**
[2nd] **Corr** | 0.85

Note that in this example the use of the r_{test} values to determine the significance of the correlation coefficient is not really valid. When determining results like the r_{test} values, one of the assumptions made is that both variables are distributed randomly with normal distribution. Since "x" in this example can only be sequential year values it is not a random variable.

A statistic that can be used with this example, however, is the coefficient of determination. The coefficient of determination is the square of the correlation coefficient. It expresses the proportion of variation in "y" explained by "x". In this example, r = .85 and r^2 = .72. Therefore 72% of the variance in "y" has been explained by the knowledge of "x".

Relating Job Performance to Test Score (Establishing Correlation)

In this example the linear regression feature of the calculator, particularly the correlation feature ([2nd] [Corr]), is used to help make a decision on whether two variables are related. It may appear that one factor is related to another, but how closely they relate may be unclear. With the calculator, you can get a more accurate picture of the relationship between two variables.

Example: Suppose your sales manager is spending a considerable sum on a test for prospective sales employees. See if this test is actually telling you anything about how well the employee will function in the field. Does a higher test score mean superior sales performance? How strong a correlation is there between these two factors in your business?

You have samples of the test scores for 10 employees, along with records on sales performance expressed as the percentage of the time that each employee exceeded his or her weekly sales goals last year. The data is tabulated below:

Employee	Employee Test Score ("x")	Employee Sales Performance ("y")
Lane	5	10
Bob	13	30
Britt	8	30
Ralph	10	40
Lana	15	60
Dae	20	50
Dennis	4	20
Patrick	16	60
Kathy	18	50
Kevin	6	20

Target: Determine if there is a relationship between test scores and sales performance. If so, what is the relationship, and how reliable is it?

Tools: The calculator's linear regression feature can easily apply some complicated statistical mathematics to this problem. First enter the data with the [x:y] and [Σ+] keys. Then study the correlation coefficient (r) by pressing [2nd] [Corr] , and consulting the "r_test" table at the end of this chapter.

RELATING JOB PERFORMANCE TO TEST SCORE (ESTABLISHING CORRELATION)

Keying it in: Enter the data and determine the correlation coefficient.

Press	Display	Comments
$\boxed{\text{ON/c}}$ $\boxed{\text{ON/c}}$ $\boxed{\text{2nd}}$ $\boxed{\text{CSR}}$	0.00	Clear display, pending operations, and statistical registers
5 $\boxed{x{:}y}$ 10 $\boxed{\Sigma+}$	1.00	
13 $\boxed{x{:}y}$ 30 $\boxed{\Sigma+}$	2.00	
8 $\boxed{x{:}y}$ 30 $\boxed{\Sigma+}$	3.00	
10 $\boxed{x{:}y}$ 40 $\boxed{\Sigma+}$	4.00	
15 $\boxed{x{:}y}$ 60 $\boxed{\Sigma+}$	5.00	
20 $\boxed{x{:}y}$ 50 $\boxed{\Sigma+}$	6.00	
4 $\boxed{x{:}y}$ 20 $\boxed{\Sigma+}$	7.00	
16 $\boxed{x{:}y}$ 60 $\boxed{\Sigma+}$	8.00	
18 $\boxed{x{:}y}$ 50 $\boxed{\Sigma+}$	9.00	
6 $\boxed{x{:}y}$ 20 $\boxed{\Sigma+}$	10.00	

To find the correlation coefficient:

$\boxed{\text{2nd}}$ $\boxed{\text{Corr}}$ 0.87   = r

Decision Time: The correlation coefficient of 0.87 indicates that there is a relatively high relationship between the test scores and the indicator for employee performance.

To determine how significant this correlation coefficient is, look at the table at the end of this chapter. Find the line for the number of samples (in this case 10) and examine the "r_{test}" values listed to the right. The value for r (the correlation coefficient: 0.87) falls between .765 and .872 listed on the table, so you can be between 99% and 99.9% confident that the correlation coefficient was not due to chance alone.

MEASURING & FORECASTING TRENDS
RELATING JOB PERFORMANCE TO TEST SCORE
(ESTABLISHING CORRELATION)

Going further: Using the data in the calculator, employee performance can be predicted for any given test
score. To do this, key in the score ("x") value and press
[2nd] **y'** . Some examples:

Press	Display	Comments
7 [2nd] **y'**	24.92	
25 [2nd] **y'**	73.23	
30 [2nd] **y'**	86.65	

If you wish to make predictions again at a later date, write down
the equation of the line the calculator has drawn through the data
using the [2nd] **b/a** and **x:y** key sequences:

Press	Display	Comments
[2nd] **b/a**	6.14	Intercept value (b)
x:y	2.68	Slope value (a)

The equation of any straight line can be expressed as:

$$y = ax + b$$
$$y = (Slope) \times (x) + (Intcp);$$ so in this case the line is given by
$$y = 2.68 \times (x) + 6.14$$

If you wish to make a prediction, you need to note the slope and intercept values. If an employee then scores 24 on the test, you can
substitute that result for "x" in the equation to predict his or her performance.

Press	Display	Comments
[ON/C] [ON/C]	0	Clear display and pending operations
2.68 [X] 24 [+] 6.14 [=]	70.46	

How to Use "r$_{test}$" Table for Correlation Coefficients

Find the number of samples in the left hand column, and scan across to the right, comparing the values of r$_{test}$ listed in the table to the calculated correlation coefficient. Find the values of r$_{test}$ that the correlation coefficient lies between and scan upward to read the "degree of certainty" limits for the coefficient. If the correlation coefficient is too small to find in the table, then you are less than 80% sure of its significance. For negative correlation coefficients, take the absolute value of the correlation coefficient and find that value in the table.

The values in this table are from the formula:

$$r_{test} = \left(\frac{t^2}{t^2 + df} \right)^{1/2}$$

where df = the degrees of freedom, and t is the t value for df from table C in the Appendix.

Example: For 15 samples, a correlation coefficient of .525 can be considered between 95% and 99% significant.

Table of "r$_{test}$" Values — Test Values for Correlation Coefficient

# of Samples	(df) degrees of Freedom	80%	90%	95%	99%	99.9%
3	1	.951	.988	.997	1.000	1.000
4	2	.800	.900	.950	.990	.999
5	3	.687	.805	.878	.959	.991
6	4	.608	.729	.811	.917	.974
7	5	.551	.669	.755	.875	.951
8	6	.507	.621	.707	.834	.925
9	7	.472	.582	.666	.798	.898
10	8	.443	.549	.632	.765	.872
11	9	.419	.521	.602	.735	.847
12	10	.398	.497	.576	.708	.823
13	11	.380	.476	.553	.684	.801
14	12	.365	.457	.532	.661	.780
15	13	.351	.441	.514	.641	.760
16	14	.338	.426	.497	.623	.742
17	15	.327	.412	.482	.606	.725
18	16	.317	.400	.468	.590	.708
19	17	.308	.389	.456	.575	.693
20	18	.299	.378	.444	.561	.679
21	19	.291	.369	.433	.549	.665
22	20	.284	.360	.423	.537	.652
23	21	.277	.352	.413	.526	.640
24	22	.271	.344	.404	.515	.629
25	23	.265	.337	.396	.505	.618
26	24	.260	.330	.388	.496	.607
27	25	.255	.323	.381	.487	.597
28	26	.250	.317	.374	.479	.588
29	27	.245	.311	.367	.471	.579
30	28	.241	.306	.361	.463	.570
31	29	.237	.301	.355	.456	.562
32	30	.233	.296	.349	.449	.554
42	40	.202	.257	.304	.393	.490
62	60	.165	.211	.250	.325	.408
122	120	.117	.150	.178	.232	.294

Testing
Claims

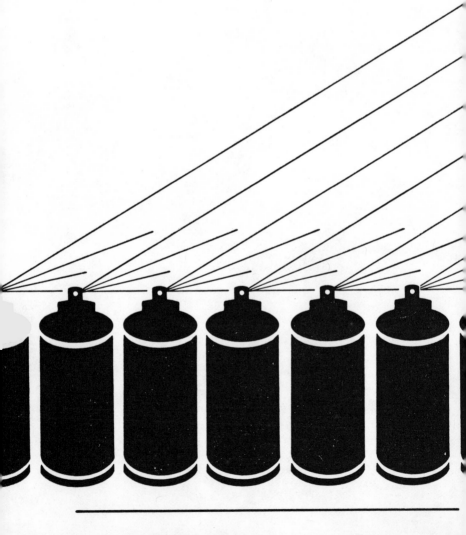

Introduction

Many times in business, science, or everyday life you must make decisions about accepting or buying large quantities of items. Time and expense usually only allow examination and testing of a few samples. This is often the case in an "incoming quality control" operation, for example.

Whenever deciding about a large population based on a small sample, a certain amount of uncertainty is present. When a manufacturer claims that goods meet a certain specification, data from the sample can be used to test that claim to a specified degree of certainty.

The examples in this chapter explore the examination and analysis of data from samples and relating that data to larger populations. Complex statistical methods are involved, but with the calculator doing the mathematics, the implementation of these techniques is quite simple.

In most of the examples in this chapter the following situation is addressed:

A manufacturer (grower/supplier, etc.) makes a claim about a particular specification for a shipment of goods he has just delivered. This claim usually is expressed as a mean value for the population:
> "The mean weight of product in these containers is 510 grams."
> "The mean lifetime of these batteries under standard load conditions is 180 hours."

To check the claim made, test as large a sample as possible, given the time and expense limitations. Then use the test data to determine and analyze the mean value and standard deviation. Your calculator has keys that make this calculation quite easy. Take the measured sample data and enter it with the ⎡Σ+⎤ key. The ⎡2nd⎤ ⎡Mean⎤ and ⎡2nd⎤ ⎡σn-1⎤ keys give the mean and standard deviation of the sample data and the first step in the decision. Is the mean close to the claimed value? Is the standard deviation large or small? If the mean is significantly lower than the claimed value, or there is a large standard deviation, indicating a highly varying value for the parameter you are examining, that may be enough reason to reject the shipment immediately.

MEAN WEIGHT OF AEROSOL DISPENSERS

The rest of this chapter shows the use of statistical inferences in calculator decision making based on sample results. These are important concepts: The *population* refers to the entire set of items under consideration; the *sample* is a part of the population that has been chosen to be tested. You will be making decisions about the population based on sample data and the *level of certainty* chosen.

Mean Weight of Aerosol Dispensers

This example involves testing the manufacturer's claim with concern about both the upper and lower limits.

A large shipment (population) of aerosol cans of insecticide has arrived at your receiving dock. The manufacturer claims that the cans contain, on the average, 510 grams of insecticide. You would like to be sure that he is meeting this claim.

You are concerned about this problem for two reasons: These particular cans do not work properly if they are too full; and you are not getting what you paid for if they are less than full. Ideally, each can contains exactly 510 grams.

Have a technician measure the weight of 40 cans (the sample) and tabulate the data. With a quick calculation on the calculator you find:

The mean sample weight is 508.75g (usually labeled $\bar{x}$)
The sample standard deviation (labeled s_x) is 19.97g

The decision: Is the manufacturer meeting his claim? Should you accept the shipment or reject it? Can the sample data give you more information on which to base your decision?

Target: Suppose you want to be 95% sure that the manufacturer has *not* met his claim before you reject the shipment. The target here is to get as much information as possible about the population, based on the data from the sample.

Tools: The sample size is over 30 items, which statisticians generally agree is an informal boundary between "large" and "small" samples. For the "large" sample of 40 items you may assume that the sample standard deviation (s_x) is an acceptable estimate of the population standard deviation (usually labeled with the lower case Greek letter sigma, σ).

MEAN WEIGHT OF AEROSOL DISPENSERS

This information often allows reaching some important conclusions immediately. Most manufacturing processes deviate from the specified or target value in a "normal" way, so the population values can be considered to follow the "normal curve." This means that about 95% of the cans will be within ±2 standard deviations of the mean. The sample standard deviation of 19.97 implies a range of almost 80 grams (from 39.94 below the mean to 39.94 above the mean) for about 95% of the cans. If a ±40 gram variation from the mean in the weight of the cans is by itself unacceptable, you might reject the cans based on the standard deviation value alone.

If the standard deviation value is acceptable, continue with the analysis.

a) Select a degree of certainty for the decision to accept or reject, in this instance 95%.

b) Establish a range within the population mean (labeled with the Greek letter mu, μ), to a particular degree of certainty. The formula for this range is:

$$\text{Range for } \mu \text{ at degree of certainty selected} = \bar{x} \pm \frac{\sigma}{\sqrt{n}} z$$

In this formula $\bar{x}$ is the sample mean, n is the number of samples, and z is the "z score" for the selected degree of certainty. This "z score" can be found in Table A in the Appendix, in column II where z values for checking both upper and lower levels are tabulated. In this table, column II reads a z value of 1.96 at a 95% degree of certainty.

Summarizing:

From Table A: z = 1.96

$\sigma = s_x = 19.97$ (for large samples only, n > 30)

n = 40

$\bar{x} = 508.75$,

and you need to evaluate $\bar{x} \pm \dfrac{\sigma}{\sqrt{n}} z$.

Keying it in: A good way to begin this calculation is to evaluate the last term $\dfrac{\sigma}{\sqrt{n}}z$ and store it in memory 0.

Press	Display	Comments
ON/c ON/c 2nd Fix 2	0.00	Clear display and pending operations and set display to two decimal places
2nd CSR	0.00	Clear statistics registers
19.97 ÷ 40 √x ×	3.16	This evaluates $\dfrac{\sigma}{\sqrt{n}}z$
1.96 = STO 0	6.19	and stores it
+ 508.75 =	514.94	Next, evaluate $\bar{x} + \dfrac{\sigma}{\sqrt{n}}z$
508.75 − RCL 0 =	502.56	Evaluate $\bar{x} - \dfrac{\sigma}{\sqrt{n}}z$

The manufacturer's claimed value of 510g falls inside these limits; therefore the claim can be accepted.

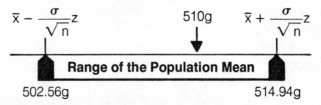

$$\bar{x} - \frac{\sigma}{\sqrt{n}}z \qquad 510g \qquad \bar{x} + \frac{\sigma}{\sqrt{n}}z$$

Range of the Population Mean

502.56g   514.94g

The sample indicates that the population mean is between these two numbers, with 95% certainty.

MEAN WEIGHT OF AEROSOL DISPENSERS

Decision time: You now have more information about the shipment based on the sample results. The mean weight value for the shipment (the whole population) lies between 502.56 grams

and 514.94 grams, with 95% certainty. Since the manufacturer's claimed weight value of 510 grams falls within these limits, as far as you can tell from the sample he has met his claim. Based on this analysis, accept the shipment of aerosol cans.

The analysis is summarized here:

a) Get as large a sample as possible and measure it; calculate the sample mean ($\bar{x}$) and standard deviation (s_x).

b) Choose the degree of certainty needed and calculate the predicted range for the population mean with the formula below:

$$\text{Range for } \mu = \bar{x} \pm \frac{\sigma}{\sqrt{n}}z$$

Find z from column II in Table A for the selected degree of certainty. For samples with over 30 items, approximate σ with s_x.

c) If the manufacturer's claim value falls inside the range, accept, and vice versa.

Further notes: When selecting the degree of certainty for a problem, it is important to know how the statistical process works. The amount of information in the sample does not change. If a very high degree of certainty is selected, then what you are certain about is less definite. Here is an example: A mechanic looks at your car and says it will cost about $80 to $100 to fix it. If you tell him to be 99% sure of his estimate, he will probably estimate a wider range, perhaps $50 to $200. If the situation under investigation demands more certainty about a smaller range, then a larger sample must be taken.

Mean Battery Lifetime

This example involves testing a manufacturer's claim with concern about meeting the minimum specifications only.

The manufacturer of an electronic product requires a battery. A supplier has shipped 5000 batteries, and claims the mean lifetime for this shipment (population) is 180 hours. The manufacturer wants to check on the supplier's claim. Critical to the decision to accept the shipment is that the mean lifetime of the shipment of batteries is no less than 180 hours.

To test the population of 5000 (N) batteries, have a technician select a sample (n) of 100 batteries and measure the average lifetime under standard load conditions. Since this test ruins the batteries, expense determines the sample size. The technician finds that the sample mean lifetime ($\bar{x}$) is 175 hours, with a sample standard deviation (s_x) of 18 hours. The decision: Accept or reject the shipment?

Since the sample of 100 batteries qualifies as a "large" one (n>30), the sample standard deviation (s_x) is considered to be equal to the population standard deviation (σ). So an immediate decision becomes: Is the standard deviation of the shipment acceptable? In this case, $\sigma = 18$ hours. Suppose this variability is acceptable. Then a judgment must be made about the population mean (μ). The sample mean ($\bar{x}$) is 175 hours. How can this information be used to draw a conclusion about the population mean lifetime?

 Target: Suppose the manufacturer wants to be 95% certain not to reject good batteries. The primary concern is that the battery life be not much less than 180 hours.

Tools: A formula from statistics allows calculating, from sample data, a range in which the population mean will lie. With this range, based on the sample data and degree of certainty, an upper and a lower limit for the actual population mean can be found.

The formula is:

$$\text{Range for population mean} = \bar{x} \pm \left[\frac{(N - n)}{(N - 1)}\right]^{1/2} \frac{\sigma}{\sqrt{n}} z$$

(This formula is complex, but it is easy to evaluate on the calculator.)

In this case: $\bar{x}$ is the sample mean lifetime = 175 hours;
N is the population size = 5000;
n is the sample size = 100;
σ is the standard deviation of the population, which in this case
  can be approximated by s_x (= 18 hours);
  and,
z is the z value found in Appendix Table A, for the degree of certainty selected (95%), taken from column I, since rejection is based on only the lower boundary in this case. The value of z is 1.65.

A note here: In this formula the expression $\left[\frac{(N - n)}{(N - 1)}\right]^{1/2}$

is a factor which allows for the fact that when batteries in the sample are tested, they are removed from the population and cannot be returned after the test. This removal of sample items affects the "randomness" of the selection, and this factor corrects for this fact.

Keying it in: In doing this calculation, first evaluate the quantity

$$\left[\frac{(N - n)}{(N - 1)}\right]^{1/2} \frac{\sigma}{\sqrt{n}} z \text{ and store it.}$$

Press	Display	Comments
ON/C ON/C	0.00	Clear display and pending operations
((5000 − 100)	4900.00	
÷ (5000 − 1)	4999.00	
) √x X 18 ÷ 100	100	
√x X 1.65 = STO 0	2.94	The deviation
+ 175 =	177.94	Upper limit
175 − RCL 0 =	172.06	Lower limit

Decision time: The population mean is therefore predicted to have a value somewhere between 172.06 and 177.94. Thus, with 95% certainty, it can be said that the population mean is not

greater than 177.94. So, based on the sample data, the battery mean lifetime is less than 180 hours, and based on this analysis the shipment should be rejected, or the vendor should be talked to about correcting the problem.

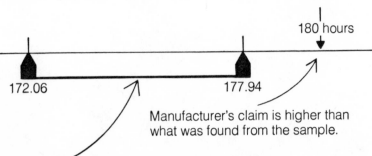

180 hours

172.06   177.94

Manufacturer's claim is higher than what was found from the sample.

The actual value of the population mean is predicted to be in this range, lower than the 180 hour lifetime needed (and claimed by the manufacturer).

The Tint in Paint Mix

This example involves testing a claim using data from a small sample with concern about both upper and lower limits.

A check is being made on a formulating process in a paint manufacturing operation concerning the amount of red dye being mixed into 5 gallon containers of rose colored paint. The process specification calls for 15.5 ounces of red tint in each can. To perform the check, select a random sample of 8 cans. Through analysis the tint content is found to be:

15.2 oz	15.8 oz
15.0 oz	16.1 oz
15.7 oz	15.6 oz
15.9 oz	15.9 oz

The analysis is expensive, so a small sample quantity is all that can be analyzed. The decision in this case: Should manufacturing be stopped and the process be adjusted?

Target: Get as much information as possible about the population mean for the amount of red tint, based on data from the small sample. To do this, use a statistical technique especially designed to handle the "small sample" situation. This technique calculates a predicted range of values within which the population mean (μ) will fall, with a selected degree of certainty.

This predicted range of values can form the basis for a decision. If the calculated range of values includes the specification value of 15.5 oz., there is not enough indication of trouble to stop production. If the range of values calculated from the sample data does not include the specification value, however, it is sure (to the degree of certainty selected) that there is a problem and an adjustment should be made. The concern is about both limits on the amount of tint; too much will give a color that is too red, while too little tint will provide too weak a color.

THE TINT IN PAINT MIX

Tools: Since the sample size in this case is less than 30, it is classified as a small sample and statistical methods especially suited to this situation should be used. First, decide on a degree of certainty needed for the decision, for instance 90%. Then, calculate the predicted range for the mean tint (population value) using the formula below.

Predicted Range for
Population Mean $\mu = \bar{x} \pm \dfrac{s_x}{\sqrt{n}} t$

where $\bar{x}$ is the mean value for the sample;
s_x is the sample standard deviation;
n is the size of the sample;
    and,
t is a value found from Table C in the Appendix for the degree of certainty selected (90%), and the number of degrees of freedom (df) for the problem. In this case df = (n − 1) = 7. Table C gives a t value of 1.895

To find the sample mean ($\bar{x}$) and sample standard deviation (s_x), use special keys on the calculator.

Keying it in: First, clear the calculator and enter the sample data with the ⎡Σ+⎤ key:

Press	Display	Comments
⎡ON/c⎤ ⎡ON/c⎤ ⎡2nd⎤ **CSR**	0.00	Clear display and pending operations. If necessary, clear the statistical registers
15.2 ⎡Σ+⎤	1.00	The display keeps track
15 ⎡Σ+⎤	2.00	of the number of data
15.7 ⎡Σ+⎤	3.00	entries
15.9 ⎡Σ+⎤	4.00	
15.8 ⎡Σ+⎤	5.00	
16.1 ⎡Σ+⎤	6.00	
15.6 ⎡Σ+⎤	7.00	
15.9 ⎡Σ+⎤	8.00	

Now calculate the sample mean and standard deviation.

Press	Display	Comments
[2nd] [Mean]	15.65	The sample mean, $\bar{x}$
[2nd] [On-1]	0.37	The sample standard deviation, s_x

The sample mean is near 15.5, and the standard deviation is low, indicating that there is a relatively low variation to the measured sample red tint values. But the sample is a small one, and an important decision must be made about a much larger population based on it. This is where the statistical method can be helpful. Now calculate the predicted range of the population mean (μ).

Predicted Range = $\bar{x} \pm \dfrac{s_x}{\sqrt{n}} t$

Now you know that $\bar{x} = 15.65$ $n = 8$
$s_x = 0.37$ $t = 1.895$

Begin by calculating $\dfrac{s_x}{\sqrt{n}} t$

Press	Display	Comments
[ON/c] [ON/c]	0.00	Clear display and pending operations
.37 [÷] 8 [√x] [X]	0.13	
1.895 [=] [STO] 0	0.25	Now add this to $\bar{x}$ to find upper range limit:
[+] 15.65 [=]	15.90	$= \bar{x} + \dfrac{s_x}{\sqrt{n}} t$
15.65 [−] [RCL] 0 [=]	15.40	$= \bar{x} - \dfrac{s_x}{\sqrt{n}} t$

 Decision time:

15.50 oz amount of red tint specified

15.40   15.90

From the small sample of 8 cans it can be stated, with 90% certainty, that the population mean value for the red tint is between 15.4 and 15.9 oz. Since the specified value of 15.5 lies between these limits, the process appears to be acceptable.

Pharmaceutical Specifications

This example involves testing a claim using data from a small sample with concern about the maximum specification only.

You are called in to help the buyer for a large chain of drugstores. A large shipment of cough medicine has arrived. The manufacturer claims that the preparation contains 8% alcohol. The buyer needs to be certain that the population's mean alcohol content is no greater than 8%. He can only get data on a small sample: 5 bottles were selected at random and analyzed. The bottles showed 7.85%, 8.33%, 7.97%, 8.31% and 7.76% alcohol upon test. Should you advise the buyer to reject the shipment? He says he would like to be 95% sure of his decision.

 Target: In this case you need to find out all you can about the population mean (μ) from the small sample. The concern is that the mean alcohol content of the shipment is not over 8%.

Tools: You are dealing with a small sample (n<30), so use the statistical analysis method suitable for small sample analysis. First enter the sample data with the $\boxed{\Sigma+}$ key, and calculate the sample mean ($\overline{x}$) and sample standard deviation (s_x) with the $\boxed{2nd}$ $\boxed{Mean}$ and $\boxed{2nd}$ $\boxed{\sigma n\text{-}1}$ keys. Next, using the formula below, calculate the predicted range for the population mean:

Predicted range for
the population mean $= \overline{x} \pm \dfrac{s_x}{\sqrt{n}} \, t$

In this formula
 $\overline{x}$ is the sample mean,
 s_x is the sample standard deviation,
 n is the number of items in the sample (5), and
 t is the "t" value found in the Appendix.

The t value is found in Table B, because you are concerned with only one limit. Locate the t value for the degree of certainty required (95%) and the number of degrees of freedom (df) equal to (n − 1)= 4. The t value is 2.132.

PHARMACEUTICAL SPECIFICATIONS

Keying it in: Enter the data using the $\boxed{\Sigma +}$ key, and calculate the sample mean and standard deviation values:

Press	Display	Comments
$\boxed{\text{ON/C}}$ $\boxed{\text{ON/C}}$ $\boxed{\text{2nd}}$ $\boxed{\text{CSR}}$	0.00	Clear display, pending operations, and statistical registers
7.85 $\boxed{\Sigma +}$	1.00	Enter the data: the calculator
8.33 $\boxed{\Sigma +}$	2.00	keeps count of the number
7.97 $\boxed{\Sigma +}$	3.00	of entered data points
8.31 $\boxed{\Sigma +}$	4.00	
7.76 $\boxed{\Sigma +}$	5.00	
$\boxed{\text{2nd}}$ $\boxed{\text{Mean}}$	8.04	The sample mean ($\bar{x}$)
$\boxed{\text{2nd}}$ $\boxed{\sigma n\text{-}1}$	0.26	The sample standard deviation (s_x)

Clear the calculator and calculate the predicted range for the population mean.

First calculate $\dfrac{s_x}{\sqrt{n}}\, t$ and store it,

then calculate $\bar{x} \pm \dfrac{s_x}{\sqrt{n}}\, t$.

Press	Display	Comments
$\boxed{\text{ON/C}}$ $\boxed{\text{ON/C}}$	0.00	Clear display and pending operations
.26 $\boxed{\div}$ 5 $\boxed{\sqrt{x}}$ $\boxed{\times}$ 2.132	2.132	
$\boxed{=}$ $\boxed{\text{STO}}$ 0	0.25	Now add x to calculate $\bar{x} + \dfrac{s_x}{\sqrt{n}}\, t.$
$\boxed{+}$ 8.04 $\boxed{=}$	8.29	Upper limit Now calculate $\bar{x} - \dfrac{s_x}{\sqrt{n}}\, t.$
8.04 $\boxed{-}$ $\boxed{\text{RCL}}$ 0 $\boxed{=}$	7.79	Lower limit

Decision time:

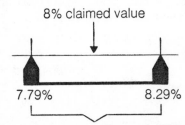

8% claimed value

7.79%   8.29%

Predicted range of the population
mean based on the small sample.

Based on the small number of samples, the actual amount of alcohol may be as low as 7.79%. Since the claimed value is 8%, you can accept the shipment. In this case the entire predicted range of the population mean would have to be greater than 8% before rejecting the shipment with 95% certainty.

Defective Parts

This example involves checking on a proportion of defective parts with concern about the maximum percentage defective only.

You are called in to aid a flashlight manufacturer. He has just received his first shipment of flashlight bulbs from a new supplier and wants to be particularly sure the shipment is good before accepting it. Testing the parts is quite simple in this case (they either light or they do not), so a sizeable sample can be easily tested. The new bulb supplier insists that the shipment (population) will contain no more than 12% defective bulbs.

The line foreman has 250 of the bulbs tested, and of these, 43 (17.2%) fail. He asks your advice: Should the shipment be accepted or rejected based on this data? He would like to be 90% sure the lot has more than 12% defective bulbs, before he rejects the shipment and looks for a new vendor.

Target: This example deals with a claim about a proportion, so you should use a statistical technique especially suited to handling the problem. First, use the formula below to calculate the predicted range of the population mean, as in previous examples. In this case, however, instead of the population mean being a numerical value (such as weight, or percent volume) it is the proportion of defective parts in the population.

The formula for the range is:

Predicted range of the

population mean proportion $= \bar{P} \pm \left(\dfrac{\bar{P}(1 - \bar{P})}{n} \right)^{1/2} z.$

where: $\bar{P}$ is the proportion of defective parts found in the sample
(In this case $\dfrac{43}{250}$ or 0.172);
n is the sample size (250);
    and,
z is the z value found from Table A in the Appendix.

Only one limit is of concern; you should reject if the shipment is over 12% defective, and accept otherwise. Since you wish to be 90% sure of a decision to reject, the z value from Table A is found from column 1 to be 1.28.

Keying it in: The proportion of defective parts in the sample is 17.2% or 0.172. Evaluate the expressions

$$\bar{P} + \left(\frac{\bar{P}(1 - \bar{P})}{n}\right)^{\frac{1}{2}} z \text{ and } \bar{P} - \left(\frac{\bar{P}(1 - \bar{P})}{n}\right)^{\frac{1}{2}} z$$

to calculate the predicted range of the mean.

Begin by evaluating $\left(\frac{\bar{P}(1 - \bar{P})}{n}\right)^{\frac{1}{2}} z$, and storing it.

For a later problem, we will need to evaluate this expression again using a different value for z. Storing the key sequence in program memory allows changing the variables and repeating the problem solution with just a few keystrokes.

First, key the problem into program memory assuming $\bar{P}$ is stored in memory 0, n in memory 1, and z in memory 2. Memory 3 is used to store the evaluation of the expression shown above.

Press	Display	Comments
ON/c ON/c INV 2nd Fix	0	Clear display and pending operations and reset to floating decimal
2nd CSR 2nd Part 4	32.4	Clear statistics registers and set partition to 32 program steps and 4 user data memories
LRN 2nd CP	00 00	Enter learn mode and clear previous program
RCL 0 ✕ (1 −		
RCL 0	08 00	Evaluate $\left(\dfrac{\bar{P}(1 - \bar{P})}{n}\right)^{\frac{1}{2}} z.$
) ÷ RCL 1 =		
√x̄ ✕	15 00	and store it in memory 3
RCL 2 = STO 3	20 00	
+ RCL 0 = R/S	25 00	R/S stops the program to display the upper limit
RCL 0 − RCL 3 =	31 00	Finish problem
RST	****	Stop, display lower limit, and reset to step 00. Because the partition has been reached, the calculator leaves the learn mode and resets to step 00. The display is restored

Now enter the known values into data memories and run the program.

Press	Display	Comments
ON/c ON/c	0	Clear display and pending operations
.172 STO 0	0.172	Store $\bar{P}$ in memory 0
250 STO 1	250	Store N in memory 1
1.28 STO 2	1.28	Store z in memory 2
2nd Fix 3	1.280	Set display to 3 decimal places
R/S	0.203	Upper limit
R/S	0.141	Lower limit

 Decision time:

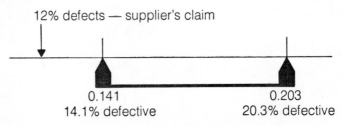

12% defects — supplier's claim

0.141
14.1% defective

0.203
20.3% defective

Predicted range for the mean percentage of defective parts in the population.

In this case the lowest expected percentage of defective parts is 14.1%. You are 90% sure that the supplier is not meeting his claim and the manufacturer's needs. Based on this analysis, you advise the foreman to reject the shipment.

Going further: The foreman is not immediately ready to return the bulbs. He needs to be very sure. (The president of the supplier is also the son-in-law of the manufacturer.) You can recheck the decision at a higher degree of certainty quite easily. Suppose you both agree that if he is 95% sure the shipment is bad it will go back. First locate the z score in table A for a 95% degree of certainty. Store the new value z in memory 2 and rerun the program.

Press	Display	Comments
1.65 STO 2	1.650	Store new z in memory 2
R/S	0.211	Upper limit
R/S	0.133	Lower limit

At 95% certainty, you would still reject the shipment.

Note that increasing the degree of certainty that the shipment contains more than 12% defective bulbs also increases the probability of not detecting whether there are more than 12% defective bulbs.

Testing for Change

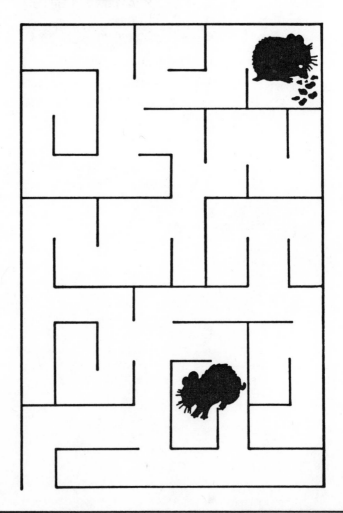

Introduction

In a variety of situations, decisions must be made concerning whether some new process or method has created a significant change when compared to an old one. Situations such as this may arise when trying new educational techniques, production methods, or engineering systems.

Sometimes the results of a change may appear to be obvious. In other cases, however, it may appear that some improvement has been made, but it is not clear that the change is enough to justify the problems that always accompany such changes. Decision-making becomes more difficult in such a situation, and a decision to endorse or institute a new procedure or process, based on data from small samples, can be difficult.

Several statistical methods are available to aid in the study of change. These methods involve some fairly sophisticated techniques, which are presented as a series of step-by-step procedures.

The statistical method being illustrated in this chapter is called a confidence interval procedure. It often is used with another procedure called the "F-test." These two procedures enable you to decide, to a selected degree of certainty, whether a significant difference exists between one set of data and another (assuming that the populations are approximately normal).

This chapter uses the F-test and confidence interval methods to analyze two case histories in order to determine whether a change or difference exists between the results of two processes.

Coated vs. Bare Pipe

This case history uses paired observations with an uncorrected "confidence interval" method for analyzing change.

A new pipe supplier claims that its coating process provides "up to three times longer life" over standard, uncoated pipe. The decision to change to a new pipe will involve a significant unit cost increase, and a pipeline several hundred miles long is to be built, so you need to be 95% certain about the decision.

The data which supports the claim is based on the results of six experiments. In each experiment a length of standard pipe and a length of coated pipe were buried side by side, in six different locations, and the weight loss due to corrosion was measured in ounces per foot per year. The results of the tests are tabulated below:

TEST DATA
(yearly weight loss in ounces/foot/year)

Uncoated Steel Pipe	Coated Pipe
3.68	2.68
1.28	0.45
1.84	0.92
3.68	1.69
1.83	0.05
6.00	0.16

 Target: Determine how much better the pipe actually is. Since the sample (6 coated and 6 uncoated pipes) is small, methods of "statistical inference" are important here. You need to predict what the mean difference in yearly weight loss would be between a coated and an uncoated pipeline, based on the experimental data (the sample) at a 95 percent degree of certainty.

Tools: First, examine the mean and standard deviation values for the pipe weight loss. Then, using the methods of statistical inference, determine the range of difference in weight loss between pipelines built of coated and uncoated pipe.

This type of data is called paired observations because each coated pipe has been paired with one uncoated pipe. By considering the difference within each pair, any differences in soils, climates, or other variables between the pairs are removed. The first step is to calculate the mean and standard deviation of the paired differences.

Keying it in: First calculate the difference between the coated and uncoated weight loss in each pair, being careful not to reverse the order of the numbers in each pair. Then find the mean and standard deviation.

If necessary, clear the statistical registers with [2nd] **CSR**.

Press	Display	Comments
[ON/c] [ON/c] [2nd] **Fix** 4	0.0000	Clear display and pending operations and fix decimal at 4 places
3.68 [−] 2.68 [=] [Σ+]	1.0000	Enter data for differences
1.28 [−] .45 [=] [Σ+]	2.0000	between coated and
1.84 [−] .92 [=] [Σ+]	3.0000	uncoated pipe
3.68 [−] 1.69 [=] [Σ+]	4.0000	
1.83 [−] .05 [=] [Σ+]	5.0000	
6 [−] .16 [=] [Σ+]	6.0000	
[2nd] **Mean**	2.0600	Mean weight loss for differences
[2nd] **σn-1**	1.9135	Standard deviation

Now use the confidence interval procedure to determine the range of difference in mean weight loss between the uncoated and coated pipe. First find the t value for the degree of surety needed (here 95%) where the degrees of freedom are $(n - 1) = 5$, since we have six paired observations. Use Table B in the Appendix because only the improvement of uncoated over coated pipe is of interest. The t value is 2.015. Now calculate the range of predicted differences for the means with the same formula used in the pharmaceutical example in Chapter 4:

$$\text{Predicted range for the population mean} = \bar{x} \pm \frac{s_x}{\sqrt{n}} \, t$$

In this case:

$\bar{x} = 2.06;$
$n = 6;$
$s_x = 1.9135;$
    and,
$t = 2.015.$

Press	Display	Comments
[ON/C] [ON/C]	0.0000	Clear display and pending operations
1.9135 [÷] 6 [√x] [X]	0.7812	Determine the value to be
2.015 [=] [STO] 0	1.5741	added and subtracted
[+] 2.06 [=]	3.6341	The upper limit
2.06 [−] [RCL] 0 [=]	0.4859	The lower limit

Decision time: Based on this analysis of the data, there is a 95% confidence that the difference in the means between a coated and an uncoated pipeline is between 3.6314 and 0.4859 ounces per foot per year. This means that, with 95% certainty, the coated pipe will perform better than the uncoated pipe by as much as 3.6314 ounces per foot per year or by as little as 0.4859 ounces per foot

per year or any value in between. This is all that can be concluded based on only six experiments. The claim of "up to three times" better performance seems to be accurate, but it could also be "as little as a few percent better performance."

With this information, consider other factors involved in changing to the new pipe, such as what extra costs are involved in changing to the coated pipe, how long the pipeline needs to last, the specific soil in which the pipe will be laid, and the other factors surrounding the decision. The analysis of this data puts you in a better bargaining position with the supplier. It also shows how much (or how little) information can be drawn from a small amount of data.

Biological Data

This example uses a corrected confidence interval method for analyzing change.

A biology student needs help in analyzing data he has taken from an experiment. He is testing to see whether a certain drug has any effect on the intelligence level of hamsters, as measured by the time it takes the hamsters to complete a simple maze test. Nine hamsters were fed the drug and given the test, while a control group of 13, which were not treated, were given the same test. The student has tabulated the data for the two groups of hamsters:

	No Drug	Treated with Drug
number of hamsters in sample	13	9
mean time to complete maze	110.01	101.58
standard deviation	9.9116	2.8566
square of standard deviation	98.24	8.16

The student's instructor maintains that there is no significant difference between the two groups. The student, however, believes that the drug did create a change, and would like to prove this with a confidence of 99%.

Target: Discover what you can conclude about the performance of the drug based on a small series of tests. Statistical inference enables you to calculate, at a selected certainty level, a confidence interval (range) concerning the difference in intelligence between hamsters treated with the drug and those not treated with the drug. The method used to calculate this range is a two part process. First, an F-test is used. Then, based on the results of this test, a "corrected" or an "uncorrected" confidence interval is calculated.

Tools: To perform the F-test, identify the data with the greatest standard deviation as the "high" data, and data with the lowest value standard deviation as the "low" data. The subscripts "H" and "L" are used to differentiate these two groups. The data, with the necessary labels, are shown below:

	No Drug	Treated with Drug
number of hamsters	$13 = n_H$	$9 = n_L$
mean time to maze test (sec)	$110.01 = \bar{x}_H$	$101.58 = \bar{x}_L$
standard deviation	$9.9116 = Sx_H$	$2.8566 = Sx_L$
square of standard deviation	$98.24 = Sx_H{}^2$	$8.16 = Sx_L{}^2$

To conduct the F-test, calculate the value of $\dfrac{Sx_H{}^2}{Sx_L{}^2}$, and compare the result to the F value found in Table E in the Appendix. (The appropriate F value in this problem is $(n_H - 1) = 12$ degrees of freedom for the numerator, $(n_L - 1) = 8$ degrees of freedom for the denominator, and a 99% degree of certainty.) This gives a value of $F = 5.67$. If the calculated value is less than this value from the table, the F-test is "passed" and you can immediately calculate the confidence interval. If, however, the calculated value is greater than the F value, a corrected confidence interval procedure must be used. The F-test used here is called a "one tailed" test, testing if $Sx_H{}^2$ is greater than $Sx_L{}^2$.

Keying it in: Begin by calculating $\dfrac{Sx_H{}^2}{Sx_L{}^2}$

Press	Display	Comments
ON/C ON/C 2nd Fix 3	0.000	Clear display and pending operations and fix display at 3 decimal places
98.24 ÷ 8.16 =	**12.039**	Value of $\dfrac{Sx_H{}^2}{Sx_L{}^2}$

Since this value is greater than the value found in the F table (5.67), the F-test is not passed, so a corrected confidence interval procedure must be used for the rest of the problem.

The correction to the confidence interval procedure provides a corrected number of degrees of freedom for the problem. Once the corrected number of degrees of freedom is calculated, the appropriate t value is used to calculate the predicted range of difference in the population means.

The corrected number of degrees of freedom is given by the formula:

$$\text{corrected degrees of freedom} = \frac{1}{\left[\frac{K^2}{(n_H - 1)} + \frac{(1 - K)^2}{(n_L - 1)}\right]}, \quad \text{where } K = \frac{\frac{Sx_H{}^2}{n_H}}{\left(\frac{Sx_H{}^2}{n_H} + \frac{Sx_L{}^2}{n_L}\right)}$$

First evaluate K:

Press	Display	Comments
[ON/c] [ON/c]	0.000	Clear display and pending operations
98.24 [÷] 13 [=]	7.557	
[STO] 0 [÷]	7.557	Value of $\frac{Sx_H{}^2}{n_H}$
[( ] [RCL] 0 [+] 8.16	8.16	
[÷] 9 [ )]	8.464	Value of denominator
[=] [STO] 1	0.893	Value of K stored in memory 1

Now calculate the "corrected" number of degrees of freedom:

Press	Display	Comments
1 [÷]	1.000	
[( ] [RCL] 1 [2nd] **x²**		
[÷] [( ]	0.797	
13 [−] 1 [ )] [+]	0.066	
[( ] 1 [−] [RCL] 1 [ )]	0.107	
[2nd] **x²** [÷]	0.011	
[( ] 9 [−] 1 [ )] [ )] [=]	14.734	The corrected number of degrees of freedom

Since the F-test was not passed, the range of difference between the two means is calculated using the formula:

$$(\bar{x}_H - \bar{x}_L) \pm \left[\frac{Sx_H^2}{n_H} + \frac{Sx_L^2}{n_L} \right]^{1/2} t$$

In this case

$\bar{x}_H = 110.01$	$\bar{x}_L = 101.58$
$n_H = 13$	$n_L = 9$
$Sx_H^2 = 98.24$	$Sx_L^2 = 8.16$

Table C only lists t values for integer values of degrees of freedom (14, 15, etc.). Using the calculator, find the appropriate value of t for 14.734 degrees of freedom using a process called interpolation.

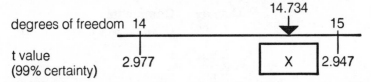

degrees of freedom	14	14.734	15
t value (99% certainty)	2.977	X	2.947

Between degrees of freedom 14 and 15, the t values go from 2.977 to 2.947. The t value for 14.734 degrees of freedom is equal to

$$2.977 - [(14.734 - 14)(2.977 - 2.947)]$$

Press	Display	Comments
ON/C ON/C	0.000	Clear display and pending operations
2.977 − ((14.734 − 14	2.977	Value of t at 14
) ×	0.734	"Distance" from 14 to 14.734
(2.977 − 2.947)	0.030	"Distance" in t values from 14 to 15
) =	2.955	t value for 14.734

With this t value, calculate the range of difference between means using the formula given previously.

Press	Display	Comments
$\boxed{\text{ON/C}}$ $\boxed{\text{ON/C}}$	**0.000**	Clear display and pending operations
110.01 $\boxed{-}$ 101.58 $\boxed{=}$		
$\boxed{\text{STO}}$ 0	**8.430**	The value of $\bar{x}_H - \bar{x}_L$ stored in memory 0
98.24 $\boxed{\div}$ 13 $\boxed{+}$	**7.557**	Next calculate the
8.16 $\boxed{\div}$ 9 $\boxed{=}$ $\boxed{\sqrt{x}}$	**2.909**	righthand term in the
$\boxed{\times}$ 2.955 $\boxed{=}$ $\boxed{\text{STO}}$ 1	**8.597**	equation
Now add $(\bar{x}_H + \bar{x}_L)$		
$\boxed{+}$ $\boxed{\text{RCL}}$ 0 $\boxed{=}$	**17.027**	Upper limit for difference between means
Subtract second term from first:		
$\boxed{\text{RCL}}$ 0 $\boxed{-}$ $\boxed{\text{RCL}}$ 1 $\boxed{=}$	**−0.167**	Lower limit for difference between means

Decision time: Based on the data, you can state with 99% certainty that the difference between the means lies between 17.027 and −0.167. If the drug had no effect on the hamsters' performance, a difference of zero between the means would be expected. Since the range of predicted values of the difference between means includes the value zero, you cannot be sure (at a

99% degree of certainty) that a change occurs when the hamsters are treated with the drug. Consequently, there is no statistically significant difference between the two groups at the 99% confidence level. Additional data might be needed to substantiate this finding.

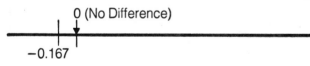

0 (No Difference)

−0.167   17.027

Going further: Would this analysis predict a significant difference between the two groups at the 95% confidence level?

Answer: Yes.

Mathematical Applications

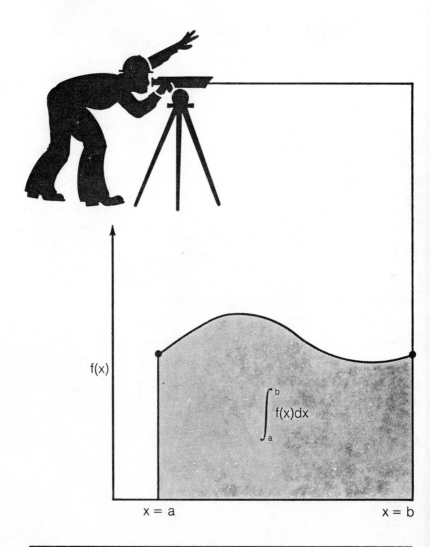

$f(x)$

$$\int_a^b f(x)dx$$

$x = a$ $x = b$

Mathematics can be fascinating and fun, but it can also turn into a tedious chore. Cumbersome numbers and repetitive calculations can obscure the interesting behavior of mathematical functions with errors and mistakes. However, with the TI-55-II handling the arithmetic, you can concentrate on the concepts and techniques of mathematics. This chapter shows a few of the ways you can apply this programmable calculator to various situations.

Area of a Triangle

Suppose you are considering buying a triangular piece of property as an investment. The owner wants $50,000 for the plot, which is bounded on all three sides by unpaved roads, but he is not sure how much land there actually is. You plan to subdivide and sell the plot by the acre, so you need an estimate of the cost per acre to predict what your profits will be. Using the odometer in your car, you find the lengths of the three sides of the plot to be 0.3, 0.5, and 0.75 miles.

 Target: You want to calculate the area of the property and the cost per acre.

Tools: The Heron formula can help solve this problem. This formula uses the lengths of the sides of the triangle to determine its area, and is written as

$$\text{Area} = \sqrt{S(S-a)(S-b)(S-c)}$$

where a, b, and c are the lengths of the sides and S is given by

$$S = \frac{1}{2}(a + b + c)$$

An acre of land is 43,600 square feet, and a square mile contains 5280^2 square feet. The conversion factor for square miles to acres is therefore

$$\frac{5280^2}{43600}$$

AREA OF A TRIANGLE

Keying it in:

Press	Display	Comments
ON/C ON/C INV 2nd Fix	0	Clear display and pending operations and reset to standard notation
.5 X (.3 + .5 + .75) = STO 0	0.8 0.775	Calculate the value of S and store it in memory 0.
X (RCL 0* − .3)	0.475	Calculate the area in square miles.
X (RCL 0 − .5) X	0.1012344	
(RCL 0 − .75) = √x	0.0503076	Area in square miles
X 5280 2nd x² ÷	1402496.7	
43600 = ÷	32.167356	Convert area to acres.
50000 x:y =	1554.3708	To divide 50000 by the area, enter the division and then exchange the x and y values. Result is the cost per acre

*As mentioned in Chapter 1, the open parenthesis can repeat a displayed number. Thus RCL 0 could be omitted here to save two keystrokes.

Pythagorean Theorem

Frequently in mathematics a special kind of triangle called a right triangle is used. A right triangle is one which has a 90° angle. Because these triangles have special conditions they also have special properties.

A Greek philosopher, Pythagoras (580-500 B.C.), developed the right triangle relation which was given his name. The Pythagorean theorem says that no matter how you draw a right triangle, the square of the longest side equals the sum of the squares of the other two sides. As a formula the Pythagorean Theorem is written $c^2 = a^2 + b^2$.

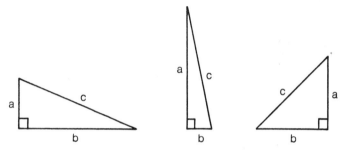

Because of this special property of right triangles, if the length of any two sides is known, the missing side is easily found. Suppose a radio antenna tower is 10 meters tall and is to be anchored by three guy wires placed six meters from the base.

6

PYTHAGOREAN THEOREM

Target: Determine the total amount of guy wire needed.

Tools: The tower makes a right angle with the ground, so the Pythagorean theorem can be used to solve for the missing side.

(length of guy wire)^2 = (height of tower)^2 + (distance along the ground)^2

(length of guy wire)^2 = $10^2 + 6^2$

length of guy wire = $\sqrt{10^2 + 6^2}$

Once the length of one guy wire is determined, multiply by three to determine the total amount needed.

Keying it in:

Press	Display	Comments
ON/c ON/c	0	Clear display and pending operations
10 2nd x^2 +	100	
6 2nd x^2 =	136	
$\sqrt{x}$	11.661904	Length of one guy wire
X 3 =	34.985711	Total length of guy wires. You need to purchase at least 35 meters

Distance Formula

The Cartesian coordinate system consists of two perpendicular lines with the horizontal line called the x-axis and the vertical line called the y-axis. The two lines intersect at the point called the origin. The "x" values to the right of the y-axis are positive and to the left of the y-axis are negative. The "y" values above the x-axis are positive and below the x-axis are negative. Thus, any point P can be represented by an ordered pair of numbers, (x,y), such that "x" is the distance from the y-axis and "y" is the distance from the x-axis. These are called the rectangular coordinates of the point P.

 Target: Find the distance between the points $(-3,-6)$ and $(4,9)$.

Tools: Rearranging the Pythagorean theorem gives an easy method of calculating the distance between any two points (x_1,y_1) and (x_2,y_2) on a graph.

$$\text{Distance} = \sqrt{(x_2 - x_1)^2 + (y_2 - y_1)^2}$$

For this example:

$$\text{Distance} = \sqrt{(4 - (-3))^2 + (9 - (-6))^2}$$

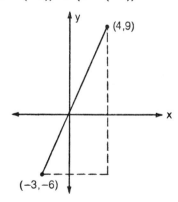

Keying it in:

Press	Display	Comments
$\boxed{\text{ON/c}}$ $\boxed{\text{ON/c}}$	0	Clear display and pending operations
$\boxed{(}$ 4 $\boxed{-}$ 3 $\boxed{+/-}$ $\boxed{)}$	7	Enter x coordinates
$\boxed{\text{2nd}}$ $\boxed{x^2}$	49	Square x coordinates
$\boxed{+}$ $\boxed{(}$ 9 $\boxed{-}$ 6 $\boxed{+/-}$ $\boxed{)}$	15	Enter y coordinates
$\boxed{\text{2nd}}$ $\boxed{x^2}$	225	Square y coordinates
$\boxed{=}$	274	Sum squares of x and y coordinates
$\boxed{\sqrt{x}}$	16.552945	The points are about 16.6 units apart

Graphing a Function

Graphs are invaluable tools for helping visualize how mathematical functions behave. Graphing even simple functions is a slow, tedious process. You must evaluate the function for one set of values, plot the point, select new values for the variables, and repeat the entire process. Even with a good non-programmable calculator, errors can distort your results. Now, however, you can program the calculator to do the computations, increment the variables, and display the resulting points.

Target: Determine how the equation $2x^2 + y = 25$ behaves over the interval from $x = 0$ to $x = 6$.

Tools: Rearrange the equation into the standard form $y = -2x^2 + 25$. Now program the calculator to solve the equation for values of x to generate a data table from which you can construct the graph.

Keying it in: The program pauses and displays the "x" value and then stops after the corresponding "y" value is displayed. When R/S is pressed again, the "x" value has been incremented by 1. The new "x" value is displayed and the corresponding "y" value is shown. The program may be repeated for as many data points as needed.

Press	Display		Comments
ON/c ON/c 2nd **Part** 2	48.2		Clear display and pending operations and partition to 48 program steps and 2 user data memories
LRN 2nd **CP**	00	00	Enter learn mode and clear previous program
2 +/− X RCL 0	05	00	
2nd **x²** + 25 =	10	00	$-2x^2 + 25$ entered into program memory with the x value to be recalled from memory 0
STO 1	12	00	Store value of y
RCL 0 2nd **Pause**	15	00	Pause, display current value for x
1 STO + 0	19	00	Add one to x value
RCL 1	21	00	Recall current value for y
RST	22	00	Stop, display value of y, and reset to step 00
LRN RST	****		Leave learn mode and reset to step 00. The display is restored

To run the program, store the starting value for "x" in memory 0. Then press R/S for as many points as you need.

Press	Display	Comments
ON/C ON/C STO 0	0	Clear display and pending operations and store starting value in memory 0
R/S	0	x_0 First x value, calculator pauses
	25	y_0 Corresponding y value
R/S	1	x_1
	23	y_1
R/S	2	x_2
	17	y_2
R/S	3	x_3
	7	y_3
R/S	4	x_4
	−7	y_4
R/S	5	x_5
	−25	y_5
R/S	6	x_6
	−47	y_6

Plotting the points and drawing the curve provides a visual representation of the behavior of $2x^2 + y = 25$ between $x = 0$ and $x = 6$. The curve starts at $y = 25$, slopes gently down through the first several data points, and then falls away at an increasing rate as x approaches the value of 6.

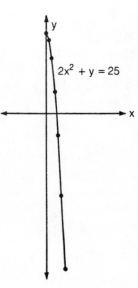

Polar/Rectangular Conversions

Another type of graph uses the polar coordinate system. The polar coordinate system consists of a point called the origin and a fixed ray radiating horizontally from the origin. Any point in the polar coordinate system may be represented by the ordered pair of numbers (r,θ) such that r is the distance from the origin to the point and θ is the angle measured from the fixed ray to the line which joins the origin and the point. θ is positive if measured counter-clockwise and negative if measured clockwise.

Points which are represented as rectangular coordinates can be converted to polar coordinates and vice versa. The TI-55-II has keys to convert from rectangular to polar and vice versa so that these two methods can be easily interchanged.

Example: A man starts at point A and travels two miles north-easterly at an angle of 30°. He then turns and travels east for five miles, turns again and travels southeasterly (−45°) for two miles, turns again and travels due south (−90°) for one mile, and completes his journey by traveling ten miles in a north-easterly (60°) direction to point B.

Target: Determine the angle for a straight trip from point A to point B and the length of a straight trip from point A to point B.

Tools: Change all the polar coordinates to rectangular coordinates and sum the x and y values. The angle from the horizontal and the distance traveled from A to B are then obtained by converting the sums back to polar coordinates.

The key sequences for the conversions are as follows:

Polar to Rectangular	Rectangular to Polar
Enter "r" coordinate	Enter "x" coordinate
Press [x:y]	Press [x:y]
Enter "θ" coordinate	Enter "y" coordinate
Press [2nd] [P→R]	Press [INV] [2nd] [P→R]
y value displayed	θ value displayed
Press [x:y]	Press [x:y]
x value displayed	r value displayed

Keying it in: In this solution the sum of the y coordinates is stored in memory 0 and the sum of the x coordinates is stored in memory 1. If the calculator is not in the degree mode, press [DRG] until DEG is displayed.

Press	**Display**	**Comments**
[ON/c] [ON/c]	0	Clear display and pending operations
2 [x:y] 30 [2nd] [P→R]	1	Enter first pair of polar coordinates and convert to rectangular coordinates
[STO] 0	1	Store y-value in memory 0
[x:y] [STO] 1	1.7320508	Store x-value in memory 1
5 [x:y] 0 [2nd] [P→R]	0	Enter second pair of polar coordinates and convert to rectangular coordinates
[STO] [+] 0	0	Add new y-value to memory 0
[x:y] [STO] [+] 1	5	Add new x-value to memory 1

(continued)

(continued)

Press	Display	Comments
2 [x:y] 45 [+/−] [2nd] [P→R]	−1.4142136	Enter third pair of polar coordinates and convert to rectangular coordinates
[STO] [+] 0	−1.4142136	Add new y-value
[x:y] [STO] [+] 1	1.4142136	Add new x-value
1 [x:y] 90 [+/−] [2nd] [P→R]	−1	Enter fourth pair of polar coordinates and convert to rectangular coordinates
[STO] [+] 0	−1	Add new y-value
[x:y] [STO] [+] 1	0	Add new x-value
10 [x:y] 60 [2nd] [P→R]	8.660254	Enter fifth pair of polar coordinates and convert to rectangular coordinates
[STO] [+] 0	8.660254	Add new y-value
[x:y] [STO] [+] 1	5	Add new x-value
[RCL] 1	13.146264	Total of x-values
[x:y] [RCL] 0	7.2460405	Total of y-values
[INV] [2nd] [P→R]	28.862951	Angle of line AB from the horizontal
[x:y]	15.010975	Distance from point A to point B

Quadratic Equations

Equations are often encountered in scientific and engineering calculations that have the form $ax^2 + bx + c = 0$. Equations of this form are known as quadratic equations. Solving for x, or finding the roots of the equation, may be done by several methods. In some cases, you may be able to factor the equation into its basic components by inspection. Sometimes, however, factoring a quadratic equation can be difficult, or nearly impossible. For example, consider the quadratic equation:

$$2x^2 + 5x + 1 = 0$$

Target: Determine the roots of the quadratic equation $2x^2 + 5x + 1 = 0$.

Tools: In cases where factoring proves difficult, you may want to use the quadratic formula, which gives the roots of any quadratic equation. It is written as

$$x = \frac{-b \pm \sqrt{b^2 - 4ac}}{2a}$$

where a, b, and c are taken from the general form of the quadratic equation $ax^2 + bx + c = 0$.

Keying it in: The following program calculates the real roots of a quadratic equation, with a in memory 0, b in memory 1, and c in memory 2. For a practical example of the use of this program see the Free Fall example in Chapter 7, Scientific Applications.

Press	Display	Comments
ON/c ON/c 2nd Part 3	40.3	Clear display and pending operations and partition to 40 program steps and 3 user data memories

(continued)

(continued)

Press	Display		Comments
[LRN] [2nd] **CP**	00	00	Enter learn mode and clear program memory
[RCL] 1 [2nd] **x²**	03	00	Determine b²
[−] 4 [×] [RCL] 0 [×] [RCL] 2	11	00	Subtract 4ac
[=] [√x] [STO] 2	15	00	Square root of b² − 4ac stored in memory 2
[−] [RCL] 1 [=]	19	00	Subtracting b from the square root is the same as $-b + \sqrt{b^2 - 4ac}$
[÷] 2 [÷] [RCL] 0 [=]	25	00	This is dividing by 2a using the advantages of AOS
[R/S]	26	00	Stop and display first root of equation
[RCL] 1 [+/−] [−] [RCL] 2 [=]	33	00	Determine $-b - \sqrt{b^2 - 4ac}$
[÷] 2 [÷] [RCL] 0 [=]	39	00	This is dividing by 2a using the advantages of AOS
[RST]		****	Display second root of equation and return to beginning of program. The calculator leaves the learn mode because all 40 programming steps have been used. The display is restored

To use the program, put a in memory 0, b in memory 1, and c in memory 2. If $b^2 - 4ac$ is negative, "Error" is displayed when the calculator attempts the square root. Note that when running the program, memory 2 is used to hold intermediate results. Therefore, to rerun the program c must be reentered in memory 2.

Press	Display	Comments
ON/C ON/C	0	Clear display and pending operations
2 STO 0	2	Store value for a
5 STO 1	5	Store value for b
1 STO 2	1	Store value for c
RST	1	Return to beginning of program
R/S	−0.2192236	First root of equation
R/S	−2.2807764	Second root of equation

Limits

A fundamental concept in calculus is the limit, which is used to investigate the behavior of a function as its variable approaches some specific value. If the limit of a function exists, it may "converge" to a single value or "diverge" to infinity. The limit of a function as its variable approaches some specific value is written mathematically as

$$\lim_{x \to h} f(x) = A$$

To determine the limit of the function, the variable x is continually made closer to the limit point h during the process, but never actually reaches it. Often, a function will have an undefined value when x is equal to h. For example, consider the limit of the natural logarithm of x divided by (x − 1) as x approaches 1.

$$\lim_{x \to 1} \frac{\ln x}{x - 1} = A$$

The limit converges to a single value, though the function has the undefined value of 0÷0 when x is equal to 1.

The calculator can easily find the limits of many functions through its ability to rapidly repeat calculations.

Target: Find the limit of the function $f(x) = \dfrac{\ln x}{x - 1}$ as x approaches 1.

Tools: This function is said to be indeterminate, since at x = 1 both ln x and (x − 1) equal zero and 0÷0 is an undefined quantity. However, you can generate a series of values for x and display them to show what happens to the value of the function as x approaches 1.

Keying it in: This program takes the current value of x from memory 0, takes half the distance between it and 1 (the value to be approached), adds it to 1, and determines the value of the function. It displays the x value being used in the function, the value of the function, and then resets to the start of the program.

Press	Display		Comments
[ON/C] [ON/C] [2nd] **Part** 1	56.1		Clear display and pending operations and partition to 56 program steps and 1 user data memory
[LRN] [2nd] **CP**	00	00	Enter learn mode and clear previous program
[RCL] 0 [−] 1 [=]	05	00	Calculate current value of x,
[÷] 2 [+] 1	09	00	stop, and display it
[=] [STO] 0 [R/S]	13	00	
[ln x]	14	00	Calculate new function value
[÷] [(] [RCL] 0 [−]	19	00	
1 [)] [=]	22	00	
[RST]	23	00	Return to beginning of program, stop, and display the new function value
[LRN] [RST]	****		Leave learn mode and reset to step 00. The display is restored

To approach the limit quickly, start with a value near 1 in memory 0.

Press	Display	Comments
1.001 [STO] 0	1.001	Store value from which approach starts
[2nd] [Fix] 4	1.0010	Fix decimal point to four places
[R/S]	1.0005	Value of x
[R/S]	0.9998	Function value
[R/S]	1.0003	New value of x
[R/S]	0.9999	New function value
[R/S]	1.0001	New value of x
[R/S]	0.9999	New function value
[R/S]	1.0001	New value of x
[R/S]	1.0000	Limit value

Going further: Occasionally you may find that the
calculator cannot arrive at a single limit value for a function. In this case, try applying L'Hospital's Rule, which
states that if the derivatives f'(x) and g'(x) of the functions f(x) and g(x) exist, then

$$\lim_{x \to h} \frac{f(x)}{g(x)} = \lim_{x \to h} \frac{f'(x)}{g'(x)}$$

In the previous example, f(x) = ln x, f'(x) = 1 ÷ x, g(x) = (x − 1)
and g'(x) = 1. Then from L'Hospital's Rule

$$\lim_{x \to 1} \frac{\ln x}{x - 1} = \lim_{x \to 1} \frac{1}{x} = 1$$

which was already found using the program.

Integrals

Finding a definite integral can be quite tedious. The TI-55-II has an integral key, however, which makes finding definite integrals easy.

Target: Find the integral of $\dfrac{dx}{\sqrt{2x-x^2}}$ from 1 to 1.5 radians.

Tools: The integral key uses Simpson's Rule (described in the Appendix) to find the definite integral. To use the integral key, enter the problem to be integrated in the program memory, followed by $\boxed{=}$ and $\boxed{R/S}$, $\boxed{RST}$, or the partition, and enter the lower limit in memory 1 and the upper limit in memory 2. Then press the $\boxed{\int dx}$ key, enter the number of divisions, and press $\boxed{R/S}$. At the end of the integration the upper limit is in both memories 1 and 2 and the answer is in the display and memory 0.

Keying it in: If the calculator is not in the radian mode, press $\boxed{DRG}$ until RAD is displayed.

Press	Display	Comments
$\boxed{ON/c}$ $\boxed{ON/c}$ $\boxed{INV}$ $\boxed{2nd}$ $\boxed{Fix}$	0	Clear display and pending operations and reset display to standard notation
$\boxed{2nd}$ $\boxed{Part}$ 3	40.3	Partition to 40 program steps and 3 user data memories
$\boxed{LRN}$ $\boxed{2nd}$ $\boxed{CP}$	00 00	Enter learn mode and clear program memory
1 $\boxed{\div}$ $\boxed{(}$ 2 $\boxed{\times}$	05 00	Enter function to be
$\boxed{RCL}$ 1 $\boxed{-}$ $\boxed{RCL}$ 1 $\boxed{2nd}$ $\boxed{x^2}$	11 00	integrated
$\boxed{)}$ $\boxed{\sqrt{x}}$ $\boxed{=}$	14 00	
$\boxed{R/S}$	15 00	Indicates the end of the function
$\boxed{LRN}$ $\boxed{RST}$	****	Leave learn mode and return to the beginning of program. The display is restored

In this example, ten intervals are sufficient to display the correct answer, and take only about 40 seconds.

Press	Display	Comments
[ON/c] [ON/c]	0	Clear display and pending operations
1 [STO] 1	1	Store lower limit
1.5 [STO] 2	1.5	Store upper limit
[∫dx]	Int 00	Asks for number of intervals
10	Int 10	Enter number of intervals
[R/S]	0.5235988	Result

Going further: Mathematicians have determined that

$$\int_{1}^{15} \frac{dx}{\sqrt{2x-x^2}} \text{ is}$$

$\cos^{-1}(1 - x)\Big|_{1}^{15}$ which is evaluated as

$\cos^{-1}(1 - 1.5) - \cos^{-1}(1 - 1) = \cos^{-1}(-.5) - \cos^{-1}(0)$.

Solving this with the calculator yields the following:

Press	Display	Comments
[ON/c] [ON/c]	0	Clear display and pending operations
.5 [+/-] [INV] [cos]	2.0943951	Arccosine of −.5
[−] 0 [INV] [cos]	1.5707963	Arccosine of 0
[=]	0.5235988	

The result is the same as when using the integral key.

Note that the correct answer cannot be obtained outside the range $0<x<2$ because the calculator may have to divide by 0.

Scientific Applications

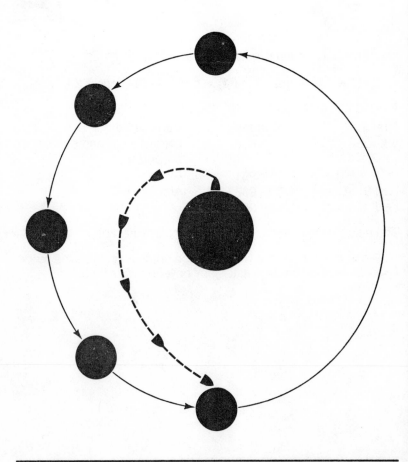

Mathematics, simple and complex, is used in applying scientific principles. The scientific principles involved may be fascinating but the tedious math may make it frustrating. The TI-55-II quickly and accurately handles the math allowing you to concentrate on the science. This chapter shows a few of the possible scientific applications.

Astronomical Numbers

Science frequently deals with very large and very small numbers. A simple way to write these numbers is in scientific notation. When a number is written in scientific notation, it is expressed as a base (the mantissa) times 10 raised to some power (the exponent). A negative mantissa indicates a negative number. A negative exponent indicates how many places the decimal point must be shifted to the left to display the number in standard notation. A positive exponent, on the other hand, indicates how many places the decimal point must be shifted to the right to display the number in standard notation.

Standard Notation	Scientific Notation
3500	3.5×10^3
1,000,000	1×10^6
.0025	2.5×10^{-3}
−456,123,000	-4.56123×10^8

The universe is so large that the light-year (the distance light travels in a year) is often used to describe it. Earth's nearest neighboring star (other than the sun) is approximately 4.3 light-years away.

 Target: Determine the length of time it would take a car, at 55 miles per hour, to travel 4.3 light years.

Tools: Light travels at the rate of 2.9979×10^8 meters per second which equals 186,281 miles per second. To solve the problem all values must be in the same unit of measurement. For this example, it is easiest to convert both units to years to obtain the number of years traveled.

Keying it in: Note that the calculator continues to calculate values in scientific notation until it is cancelled by pressing [INV] [EE], [ON/c], or turning the calculator off and back on.

Press	Display	Comments
[ON/c] [ON/c]	0	Clear display and pending operations
[(] 1.86281 [EE] 5 [X]		
60	60	
[X] 60 [X] 24 [X]		
365.25	365.25	
[X] 4.3 [)] [÷]	2.52779 13	4.3 light-years in miles
[(] 55 [X] 24 [X]		
365.25 [)]	4.8213 05	Miles traveled in year at 55 miles per hour
[=]	5.2429634 07	Years needed to travel 4.3 light-years displayed in scientific notation
[INV] [EE]	52429634	Result in standard notation

Do not clear or turn off the calculator. The previous result is used in the next example.

Going further: Astronauts going to the moon have traveled at about 25,000 miles per hour. That's much faster than the 55 mile per hour speed limit but even at this speed it takes a long time to reach the next star.

Using the value already in the display from the previous calculation, multiply by 55 miles per hour and divide by 25,000 miles per hour. The result is the time in years it takes to travel 4.3 light-years at a speed of 25,000 miles per hour.

Keying it in:

Press	Display	Comments
⊠ 55 ÷ 2.5 EE 4		
=	**1.153452 05**	Result in years displayed in scientific notation
INV EE	115345.2	Result in standard notation

Electrical Resistance and Ohm's Law

Appliances are plugged into wall outlets connected in parallel across the house supply voltage. George Simon Ohm (1787-1854), a German physicist, wrote a pamphlet on electric currents. The most important part is now called Ohm's Law. It states that E (the voltage in the outlet) = I (the total current that will flow measured in amperes) times R (the total resistance measured in ohms, Ω).

Five appliances with individual resistances of 5 ohms, 12 ohms, 17 ohms, 23 ohms, and 49 ohms respectively are plugged into house wall outlets. Assuming the house supply voltage is 115, an electrician would draw a diagram like the one below.

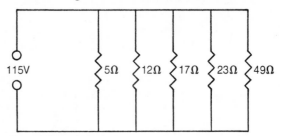

Target: Determine the current that the five appliances will draw if they are all turned on at the same time.

Tools: Solving for I (total current that will flow) in Ohm's Law obtains I = E÷R. Before using this formula, however, you need to determine R (the total resistance).

The law of parallel resistors states that $1 \div R_t = 1 \div R_1 + 1 \div R_2 + 1 \div R_3 + ...$ Substituting the known resistor values into this formula, gives the total resistance. When combined with Ohm's Law, the total current drawn may be obtained.

Keying it in:

Press	Display	Comments
ON/C ON/C	0	Clear display and pending operations
5 2nd 1/x +	0.2	
12 2nd 1/x +	0.2833333	
17 2nd 1/x +	0.3421569	
23 2nd 1/x +	0.3856351	
49 2nd 1/x =	0.4060433	Result is $1/R_t$
2nd 1/x STO 0	2.4627916	The reciprocal of $1/R_t$ gives the total resistance. It is then stored in memory 0
115 ÷ RCL 0 =	46.694978	Total current in amperes

Going further: Many people leave a light burning all the time. Suppose a 100-watt bulb is being used. How much would be saved in a year by switching to a 60-watt bulb at the rate of 6 cents per kilowatt hour?

The cost for one hour is the bulb wattage divided by 1000 times the cost per kilowatt hour. Then the cost per year is the cost for one hour times the hours in a day times the days in a year.

Press	Display	Comments
[ON/C] [ON/C]	0	Clear display and pending operations
60 [÷] 1000 [X] .06 [=]	0.0036	Cost for one hour with 60 watt bulb
[X] 24 [X] 365.25 [=] [STO] 0	31.5576	Cost for year for 60 watt bulb stored in memory 0
100 [÷] 1000 [X] .06 [=]	0.006	Cost for one hour with 100 watt bulb
[X] 24 [X] 365.25 [=]	52.596	Cost for year for 100 watt bulb
[−] [RCL] 0 [=]	21.0384	Amount saved in one year by switching to a 60-watt bulb

Vectors

Vectors have a wide variety of applications in practical physics and provide a way to visualize problems. Vectors are measurable quantities that have both magnitude and direction. A vector is shown in a diagram by a directed line segment whose direction represents the direction of the vector and whose length represents its magnitude. Without the vector diagram, the next example would be more difficult to understand.

You wish to fly a small airplane to a city that is 800 miles directly north of your home airfield. The weather service has advised you that the prevailing winds at your cruising altitude are from the west and average 50 miles per hour. Before you can file an accurate flight plan, you need to know what your groundspeed will be, how long the flight will last at your true airspeed (the speed of the airplane relative to the air) of 220 miles per hour, and in what direction, or heading, you should fly.

 Target: Determine the effect of a 50 mile per hour crosswind on your flight.

Tools: A good way to visualize this problem is to draw a vector diagram to scale, as shown. Vector AC illustrates the true airspeed ($\overline{TAS}$). Vector CB illustrates the crosswind speed ($\overline{WS}$), while vector AB shows the groundspeed vector ($\overline{GS}$). The angle θ is the heading angle taken to counteract the wind.

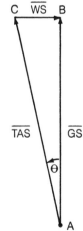

A problem like this, with different distances, true airspeeds, and crosswind speeds, may need to be solved many times, so it is appropriate to write a program. This program calculates the groundspeed in miles per hour using the Pythagorean theorem. It then determines the length of time the flight takes in hours by dividing the distance by the groundspeed. Finally the heading angle in degrees is calculated by taking the arctangent of the result of vector CB divided by vector AB.

Keying it in: The following program assumes that the true air-speed is in memory 0, the crosswind is in memory 1, and the distance to the airport is in memory 2.

If the calculator is not in the degree mode, press DRG until DEG is displayed.

Press	Display	Comments
ON/c ON/c	0	Clear display and pending operations
2nd Part 4	32.4	Partition to 32 program steps and 4 user data memories
LRN 2nd CP	00 00	Enter learn mode and clear program memory
RCL 0 2nd x^2 −	04 00	Recall and square true airspeed
RCL 1 2nd x^2 =	08 00	Recall and square crosswind
√x STO 3 R/S	12 00	Groundspeed in miles per hour stored in memory 3
RCL 2 ÷	15 00	Recall distance to airport
RCL 3 = R/S	19 00	Length of time flight takes in hours
RCL 1 ÷	22 00	Recall crosswind
RCL 3 =	25 00	Recall groundspeed
INV tan	27 00	Heading angle in degrees
RST	28 00	Stop, display the heading angle, and reset to step 00
LRN RST	****	Leave learn mode and re-set to step 00. The display is restored

Before running the program, the true airspeed must be put in memory 0, the crosswind in memory 1, and the distance to the airport in memory 2. The groundspeed will be stored in memory 3 after calculation.

Press	Display	Comments
220 [STO] 0	220	Store true airspeed in memory 0
50 [STO] 1	50	Store crosswind in memory 1
800 [STO] 2	800	Store distance to airport in memory 2
[R/S]	214.24285	Groundspeed in miles per hour
[R/S]	3.7340802	Length of time flight takes in decimal hours
[INV] [2nd] [DMS-DD]	3.4402689	Length of time flight takes in hours/minutes/seconds: 3 hours 44 minutes and 2.689 seconds
[R/S]	13.136559	Heading angle in degrees

Free Fall

Galileo Galilei (1564-1642) discovered in the 17th century that all objects fall with constant acceleration due to the force of gravity. The acceleration due to gravity is usually labeled with the letter g and is equal to 9.81 m/s², or 32.2 ft/s².

Target: Suppose a rock is thrown into a well 214 meters deep (d) at an initial velocity of 4 m/s (V_o). Determine how much time will pass before the rock hits the bottom of the well.

Tools: The formula for distance fallen is $d = 1/2gt^2 + V_ot$ where g is the gravitational constant, t is the time, and V_o is the starting velocity. This formula may be written as a quadratic equation $1/2gt^2 + V_ot - d = 0$. The quadratic equation for this example is $1/2(9.81)t^2 + 4t - 214 = 0$. Using the quadratic formula to solve for t gives

$t = (-b \pm \sqrt{b^2 - 4ac}) \div 2a$, where
$a = 1 \div 2 \times 9.81$ meters per second squared,
$b = 4$ meters per second, and
$c = -214$ meters.

Using the program for the quadratic formula given in Chapter 6, Mathematical Applications, gives the two roots. Since time cannot be negative in this example, the positive root is the time it takes the rock to hit the bottom of the well.

Keying it in:

Press	Display	Comments
ON/c ON/c 2nd Part 3	40.3	Clear display and pending operations and set partitioning to 40 program steps and 3 user data memories
LRN 2nd CP	00 00	Enter learn mode and clear program memory
RCL 1 2nd x²	03 00	b^2
− 4 X RCL 0		
X RCL 2	11 00	Subtract 4ac
= √x STO 2	15 00	Square root of $b^2 - 4ac$ stored in memory 2
− RCL 1 =	19 00	Subtracting b from the square root is the same as $-b + \sqrt{b^2 - 4ac}$
÷ 2 ÷ RCL 0 =	25 00	This is dividing by 2a using the advantages of AOS
R/S	26 00	Stop and display first root of equation
RCL 1 +/− − RCL 2 =	33 00	$-b - \sqrt{b^2 - 4ac}$
÷ 2 ÷ RCL 0 =	39 00	This is dividing by 2a using the advantages of AOS
RST	****	Display second root of equation and return to beginning of program. The calculator leaves the learn mode because all program steps have been used. The display is restored

To use the program, enter the values of a, b, and c in memories 0, 1, and 2 respectively.

Press	Display	Comments
ON/C ON/C	0	Clear display and pending operations
9.81 ÷ 2 = STO 0	4.905	Calculate value of a and store in memory 0
4 STO 1	4	Store b in memory 1
214 +/− STO 2	−214	Store c in memory 2
RST	−214	Return program counter to beginning of program
R/S	6.2100476	First root of equation
R/S	−7.025542	Second root of equation

It takes approximately 6.2 seconds for the rock to hit the bottom of the well.

Radioactive Half-Life

The number of radioactive atoms left in a material after some time (t) in seconds is given by the disintegration formula $N_t = N_o e^{-kt}$. N_t is the number of atoms left after time t, N_o is the number of atoms in the original sample, e is the special number which is equal to 2.71828..., and k is the disintegration constant.

Half-life (T) is the time it takes for half the sample of radioactive material to disintegrate. Substituting $\frac{N_o}{2}$ for N_t and T for t in the formula above gives, $\frac{N_o}{2} = N_o e^{-kT}$. Solving this equation for T gives $.5 = e^{-kT}$. Taking the natural log of both sides gives ln (.5) $= -kT$. Thus $T = \frac{\ln .5}{-k}$.

Target: Given that the disintegration constant (k) of radium is 1.36×10^{-11}/s, find its half-life.

Tools: To find half-life, use the disintegration constant in the formula derived above.

Keying it in:

Press	Display	Comments
ON/c ON/c	0	Clear display and pending operations
.5 lnx ÷	−0.6931472	
1.36 +/− EE 11 +/−	−1.36 −11	
=	5.0966704 10	Half-life in seconds displayed in scientific notation
÷ 60 ÷ 60 ÷ 24	24	
÷ 365.25 =	1.6150374 03	
INV EE	1615.0374	Half-life in years

Going further: What fraction of the radium remains after two years? To find the fraction of radium remaining use the formula $N_t = N_o e^{-kt}$. Dividing both sides by N_o, gives $\dfrac{N_t}{N_o} = e^{-kt}$ where t must be in seconds. Therefore, two years must be converted to seconds before using it in this formula.

Keying it in:

Press	Display	Comments
[ON/c] [ON/c]	0	Clear display and pending operations
2 [✕] 365.25 [✕] 24	24	
[✕] 60 [✕]	1051920	Calculate two years
60 [=]	63115200	in seconds
[✕] 1.36 [+/−] [EE] 11		
[+/−]	−1.36−11	
[=] [INV] [lnx]	9.99142−01	The result displayed in scientific notation. Note that [INV] [lnx] is equal to e^x
[INV] [EE]	0.999142	Result in standard notation

Therefore 99.91% of the radium remains after 2 years.

Conduction

Some substances are better conductors of heat than others. The ability of a substance to conduct heat is its thermal conductivity. The thermal conductivity (k) is the number of kilocalories that pass from one face to the opposite face of a one meter cube in one second if the faces have a temperature difference of one degree Celsius. This is written mathematically as $k = \dfrac{\text{Kcal/sq meter sec.}}{\text{C°/meter}}$

A kilocalorie (Kcal) is the amount of heat required to raise one kilogram (Kg) of water one degree Celsius. If the thermal conductivity of an object is known, the amount of heat transfered through that object can be determined.

Target: A glass window pane is 1m by 1m and 5 mm thick. If snow outside the window maintains the outer surface at 32° F, and the heat from the room maintains the inner surface at 41° F, how much heat is conducted through the window in 24 hours?

Tools: The formula for the amount of heat conducted through an object is

$$H = k \frac{A\Delta t}{L} s$$

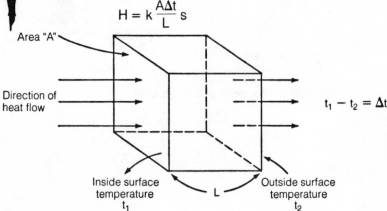

Area "A"

Direction of heat flow

$t_1 - t_2 = \Delta t$

Inside surface temperature t_1

L

Outside surface temperature t_2

In this formula A is the cross section area perpendicular to the heat
transfer, L is the length, the change in temperature from one face
to the other gives Δt, and s is the time interval in seconds. The
thermal conductivity (k) of glass is 2.5×10^{-4} Kcal/ms C°. The
thermal conductivity is calculated with Celsius degrees, so the
temperatures must be converted to Celsius when being used with
this formula.

Keying it in:

Press	Display	Comments
[ON/c] [ON/c]	0	Clear display and pending operations
2.5 [EE] 4 [+/−] [X]	2.5−04	Enter thermal conductivity
1 [2nd] [x²] [X]	2.5−04	Enter area
[( ] 41 [2nd] [°F-°C] [−]	5 00	Enter first temperature and convert to Celsius
32 [2nd] [°F-°C] [ )]	5 00	Subtract second temperature after converting to Celsius
[÷] .005 [X]	2.5−01	Divide by the length in meters
24 [X] 60 [X] 60	60	Multiply by 24 hours calculated in seconds
[=]	2.16 04	Result displayed in scientific notation
[INV] [EE]	21600	Result in Kilocalories

Moment of Inertia

Moment of inertia is the sum of the product of the mass of each particle in a rigid body and the square of its distance from an axis. The process of summing the individual moments of inertia is carried out by integration.

Target: Find the moment of inertia about the center of mass of a uniform disk with a mass of 5 kilograms, radius of 0.1 meter, and length of 1 meter.

Tools: The moment of inertia of a uniform disk about the center of mass is given by

$$I = 2\pi L \rho \int_0^R r^3 \, dr$$

The density, ρ, is the mass divided by the volume of the disk

$$\rho = \frac{M}{\pi R^2 L}$$

where
M is the total mass (5 Kg),
R is the radius of the disk (.1 m), and,
L is the length of the disk (1 m).

To use the integral key, partition the calculator for 40 program steps and 3 user data memories, enter r^3 into the program memory followed by $\boxed{=}$ and $\boxed{R/S}$, enter 0, the lower limit, in memory 1, and .1, the upper limit, in memory 2. Then press the $\boxed{\int dx}$ key, enter the number of divisions, and press $\boxed{R/S}$. At the end of the integration, the upper limit will be in both memories 1 and 2 and the answer to the integral will be in the display and memory 0. This integral must then be multiplied by 2π, the length (L), and the density (ρ).

Keying it in:

Press	Display	Comments
ON/C ON/C 2nd **Part** 3	40.3	Clear display and pending operations and partition to 40 program steps and 3 user data memories
LRN 2nd **CP**	00 00	Enter learn mode and clear program memory
y^x 3 =	03 00	Enter function to be integrated
R/S	04 00	Indicates the end of the function
LRN RST	****	Leave learn mode and return to the beginning of the program. The display is restored
0 STO 1	0	Store lower limit in memory 1
.1 STO 2	0.1	Store upper limit in memory 2
∫dx	Int 00	Asks for number of integrals
5	Int 05	Enter number of integrals
R/S	0.000025	Result of integration
X 2 X π X 1	1	Multiply by $2\pi L$
X (5 ÷ (π	3.1415927	Multiply by the density
X .1		
2nd **x²** X 1 =	0.025	Result in Kgm²

Statistical
Theory

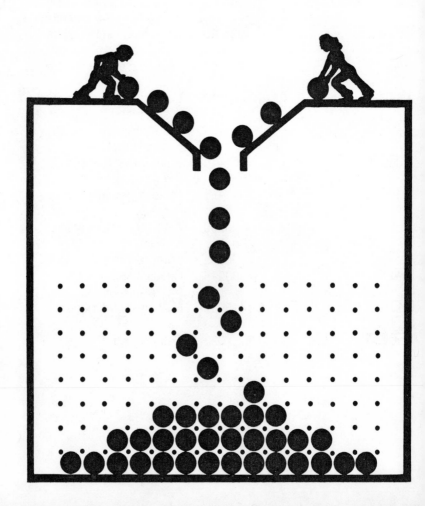

As mentioned in the introduction, the primary focus of this book is how to use statistical tools that are applicable in a variety of business, scientific, and everyday life situations. These techniques can be valuable (and even enjoyable) in bringing more accuracy into decision making with your calculator.

Understanding the why and how of these processes would involve an extended statistics course. Some sources for further reading are suggested in the Bibliography. The following is a quick survey of the key elements of the statistics used in this book.

Small Population

To see a simple example of the theory, start with an analysis of a small body of data that can be handled completely. Consider the test scores for 5 people on a simple exam (statisticians would say that this population consisted of 5 elements). Out of a perfect score of 10, the scores for the students are 4, 5, 6, 7, and 8. The calculator can quickly and easily calculate the *population mean* (labeled μ) and the *population standard deviation* (labeled σ).

Press	Display	Comments
ON/c ON/c 2nd CSR	0	Clear display, pending operations and statistical registers
2nd Fix 2	0.00	Set display to 2 decimal places
4 Σ+	1.00	
5 Σ+	2.00	Calculator keeps a count
6 Σ+	3.00	of the data entries.
7 Σ+	4.00	
8 Σ+	5.00	

Find the population mean (μ)

2nd Mean	6.00	

Find the population standard deviation (σ)

2nd σn	1.41	

With this small population, all the data can be easily and directly analyzed as illustrated below.

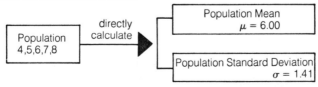

Population 4,5,6,7,8 → directly calculate →

Population Mean
$\mu = 6.00$

Population Standard Deviation
$\sigma = 1.41$

Large Population

Often the population is made up of thousands (or even millions) of items. Even with the calculator helping, entering all that data may be very difficult. In addition, sometimes the measurement may destroy the item. For example, suppose the lifetime of a shipment of batteries is being tested. To test a battery requires depleting it. Doing this to the entire population tells exactly what the mean lifetime for the population is, but also destroys the batteries.

One alternative, in situations like this, is to select a smaller number of items from the population — a sample — and test them. This is where the science of statistics comes in. Based on analyzing the smaller sample, which is cheaper, easier, and more practical than testing the population, methods of statistical inference can be used to make statements about the population mean (μ). The first step is to calculate the sample mean ($\bar{x}$) and the sample standard deviation (s_x). Then statistical techniques are used to determine information about the population, as diagrammed below.

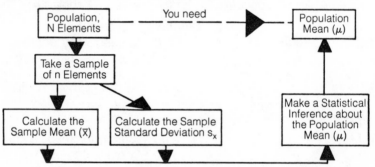

The process of using sample data to determine information about the population contains some chance. The larger the sample, the more likely that your statements about the mean are accurate.

THE SAMPLE AND THE POPULATION

The Sample and the Population

When a small sample is taken from a large population, how representative is it? In the battery example, if the sample contains many batteries with a low lifetime, an entire shipment could be underrated based on their performance. Similarly, if only batteries with a long lifetime are selected, the shipment may be overrated. The following discusses the chances that the sample mean ($\bar{x}$) is near the population mean (μ).

To understand how statisticians study this situation, consider the small population of 5 test scores. Suppose samples of 2 test scores are taken from it and examined. (In practice a population this small would not be handled using statistics, but using it to examine the processes statisticians use demonstrates some important concepts.)

The 5 test scores are 4, 5, 6, 7, 8. The population mean (μ) is 6. What happens if 2 of these scores are selected at random (a sample), and their mean ($\bar{x}$) is determined? What are the chances that the sample mean is also 6, equal to the population mean?

To answer this question, examine all the possible samples of two test scores that can be drawn out of the population of 5, and then note the sample means for each possibility. This is the way statisticians first began looking at the problem of statistical inference. All of the possible samples of 2 test scores are listed in the table below, along with their means.

The method of selection for the test scores at random could be visualized in this way: Put each score on a slip of paper; put the papers into a hat, shake well, pick one out and note it; replace it in the hat; shake again; pick again. The replacement is important. When samples are taken without replacement, a correction factor must be entered into statistical inferences.

Population of 5 Test Scores: 4, 5, 6, 7, 8

The following table lists all possible ways of picking a sample of 2 elements and the mean of each sample.

All Possible Samples of 2 Elements	Value of the Mean for Each Sample	Label for Mean Value
4, 4	4.0	$\overline{X}_1$
4, 5	4.5	$\overline{X}_2$
4, 6	5.0	$\overline{X}_3$
4, 7	5.5	$\overline{X}_4$
4, 8	6.0	$\overline{X}_5$
5, 4	4.5	$\overline{X}_6$
5, 5	5.0	$\overline{X}_7$
5, 6	5.5	$\overline{X}_8$
5, 7	6.0	$\overline{X}_9$
5, 8	6.5	$\overline{X}_{10}$
6, 4	5.0	$\overline{X}_{11}$
6, 5	5.5	$\overline{X}_{12}$
6, 6	6.0	$\overline{X}_{13}$
6, 7	6.5	$\overline{X}_{14}$
6, 8	7.0	$\overline{X}_{15}$
7, 4	5.5	$\overline{X}_{16}$
7, 5	6.0	$\overline{X}_{17}$
7, 6	6.5	$\overline{X}_{18}$
7, 7	7.0	$\overline{X}_{19}$
7, 8	7.5	$\overline{X}_{20}$
8, 4	6.0	$\overline{X}_{21}$
8, 5	6.5	$\overline{X}_{22}$
8, 6	7.0	$\overline{X}_{23}$
8, 7	7.5	$\overline{X}_{24}$
8, 8	8.0	$\overline{X}_{25}$

In a real situation, you would only know *one* of these results. You would have chosen a sample, determined its mean value ($\overline{x}$), and from that result be trying to calculate or deduce the population mean value (μ). Look for a moment at the sample mean values. The population mean is 6. What appear to be the chances of picking an $\overline{x}$ of 6 at random?

POPULATION OF 5 TEST SCORES: 4, 5, 6, 7, 8

The picture below shows how the sample means (the $\bar{x}$'s) vary by putting each mean value in its place.

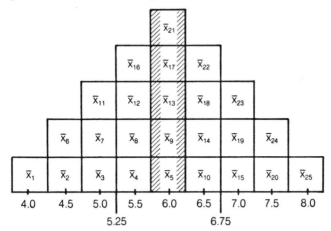

Values for the Sample Means

In this picture there is a mean label inside each little box. The boxes are stacked according to the value of their means. This picture represents the chances, for a sample picked at random, of finding one with a sample mean equal to the population mean value of 6. Five of the sample means ($\bar{x}_{21}$, $\bar{x}_{17}$, $\bar{x}_{13}$, $\bar{x}_9$ and $\bar{x}_5$, in the center boxes) each have mean values of 6. In fact, the most probable choice is a value of 6. For large populations (N over 100) and large samples (n over 30), the general rule is:

The most probable value of $\bar{x}$ is the population mean (μ).

Relative Areas

The relative areas of the boxes illustrate the chances that a sample chosen at random will have a $\bar{x}$ of 6. There are 25 boxes and 5 of them contain 6's, so the chances are the ratio of the shaded boxes to the total area of all the boxes, $\frac{5}{25}$ or 20%.

This picture also shows the chances of obtaining values of $\bar{x}$ that are close to μ. The chances of picking a sample at random whose $\bar{x}$ was 6 ± 0.75 (an x value from 5.25 to 6.75) can be determined by counting the boxes containing $\bar{x}$'s between 5.25 and 6.75, and dividing by the total number of boxes. The chances in this case are $\frac{13}{25}$ or 52%.

Consider what would happen to our picture if the number of elements in the population increased from 5 to 100, and the sample size increased from 2 to 30. Arranging all the sample means pictorially would show something like the behavior shown below.

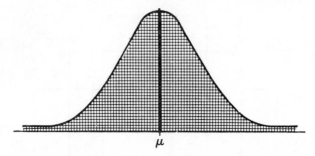

μ

As the boxes get smaller and smaller (they would be very small in this case, for with N=100 and n=30 there are 10^{60} boxes), the outside of the picture smooths out into a classic, symmetric shape called the *Normal Curve*. As a general rule, it is assumed in most situations that the $\bar{x}$'s are distributed normally (follow the normal curve) whenever the population has over 100 elements and the sample size is greater than 30.

The Normal Curve

Much has been written about the normal (or "Bell" or "Gaussian") curve. The important part is the areas under the curve, and how they can be used to obtain information about the population mean from the sample mean. Another key element in the normal curve is the standard deviation of the sample means, labeled $\sigma_{\bar{x}}$.

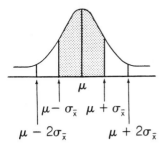

Because the sample means follow this normal behavior (for large populations and samples) some mathematical predictions can be made that apply to almost all situations where large populations and samples are concerned. These results were calculated by statisticians examining areas under the normal curve.

First, examine the normal curve above and note that it is partitioned into 4 sections, each of which is separated by $\sigma_{\bar{x}}$. The shaded area includes all the sample means whose values are between $\mu - \sigma_{\bar{x}}$ and $\mu + \sigma_{\bar{x}}$. The ratio of this area to the total is 68.26%. Whenever a sample is chosen from a population, the chances are 68.26 out of 100 that its sample mean is within $\pm \sigma_{\bar{x}}$ of the population mean. Another way of saying this is that you can be 68.26% sure that the population mean lies somewhere in the range of the sample mean plus or minus $\sigma_{\bar{x}}$.

The standard deviation of the sample means ($\sigma_{\bar{x}}$), is fairly easy to calculate from sample data. For samples with larger than 30 elements (n > 30), $\sigma_{\bar{x}}$ can be considered equal to $\dfrac{s_x}{\sqrt{n}}$, where s_x is the sample standard deviation.

The sample standard deviation is readily available. It is the number displayed after entering the sample data (with the ⌈Σ+⌋ and ⌈2nd⌋ **Frq** keys), and then pressing ⌈2nd⌋ **On-1**.

Determining the Predicted Range for μ

With the help of the normal curve, a population can be analyzed, based on a sample, in the following way.

First find the sample mean ($\bar{x}$) and sample standard deviation (s_x) by entering the sample data into the calculator with the [Σ+] and [2nd] [Frq] keys and then using the [2nd] [Mean] and [2nd] [σn-1] keys. Then, with 68.26% certainty, the population mean (μ) lies between

$$\bar{x} + \frac{s_x}{\sqrt{n}} \text{ and } \bar{x} - \frac{s_x}{\sqrt{n}} \ .$$

That is, the sample data can be used to determine a predicted range for the population mean. This range is as close as possible to the population mean, because of the uncertainty in the process of using sample data to draw conclusions about the population. It can only be stated that, to a certain degree of certainty, the population mean lies somewhere in that range.

Analyzing with Large Samples: z Scores

The predicted range for the population mean above gives the limits for the value of μ to one specific degree of certainty: 68.26%. In most applications it is useful to be able to select the degree of certainty desired (or needed) when making any decision about a population based on sample data.

Tables have been constructed based on the areas under different portions of the normal curve. These tables are called tables of "z values" or "z scores", and they enable calculating a predicted range for μ to a selected degree of certainty. (A z value table is included in the Appendix.)

To use the table, decide how sure you need to be that the calculated range includes the population mean. Check in the z table to find the appropriate z score.

Upper/Lower Limits

Two columns are included in the z table. The column used to find the z score depends on the particular decision situation, as shown in the examples in this book. If the decision involves just an upper or lower value for μ, just one limit, use column I. Otherwise, use column II.

To understand why the z values are different for these two situations, consider the normal curve.

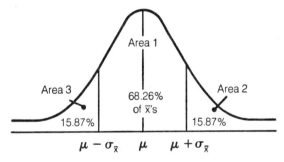

The chance of picking an $\bar{x}$ in area 1 (range $\mu \pm \sigma_{\bar{x}}$) is 68.26%, as discussed earlier. Looking at this another way, the chance of picking

an $\bar{x}$ outside of area 1 is $\dfrac{\text{area 2} + \text{area 3}}{\text{total area}}$ or $\dfrac{15.87\% + 15.87\%}{100\%}$

or about $\dfrac{32}{100}$. What is the chance of picking an $\bar{x}$ greater than

$\mu + \sigma_{\bar{x}}$ (checking only an upper limit)? The chance is

$\dfrac{\text{area 2}}{\text{total area}}$ or $\dfrac{15.87\%}{100\%}$ or about $\dfrac{16}{100}$. Since different proportions

of the total area are used, different z scores must be used for these two situations, so two columns are provided in the table.

Procedure for Using z Tables to Calculate the Range for μ

After locating the z score, the predicted range for μ can be calculated using the general formula below.

Predicted range for $\mu = \bar{x} \pm \dfrac{s_x}{\sqrt{n}} z$

where $\bar{x}$ is the sample mean and s_x is the sample standard deviation.

NOTE: For large samples the sample standard deviation (s_x) is nearly equal to the population standard deviation (usually labeled σ). The formula for the range is always correct when written with σ in place of s_x and is quite often written that way in textbooks. z is the z score for the selected degree of certainty.

This particular technique works only for large samples taken from larger populations. (The boundary line for large samples is usually considered 30 elements, and a large population is 100 or more elements.)

Analyzing with Small Samples: t Scores

As the number of samples goes below 30, the normal curve can no longer be accurately used to describe the distribution of the sample means. Statisticians have found a different family of curves that does work (if the population is nearly normally distributed) called t curves.

The shape of any t curve depends on what is called the number of *degrees of freedom* (df) for a particular sample. The number of degrees of freedom in most cases is equal to the number of elements in the sample minus one (df = n − 1). The shapes of various t curves are shown in the figure below. Note that for a very large number of degrees of freedom (essentially df = 31 or greater), the t curve becomes the normal curve and z scores can be used.

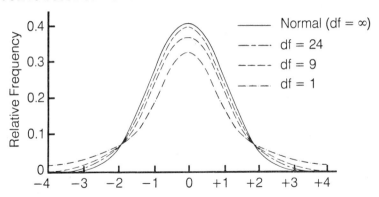

Areas under the t curves have also been tabulated in t score tables in tables B and C in the Appendix. With t scores, small sample data can be analyzed in much the same way as large sample data is analyzed with z scores. Here is the procedure to follow:

With the aid of the calculator, determine the sample mean ($\bar{x}$) and sample standard deviation (s_x).

With this information, you calculate a predicted range for the population mean. Decide how certain you want (or need) to be that the population mean will be in the predicted range. For this level of certainty look up the appropriate t score in Table B or C in the Appendix. (Use Table B if the decision involves only a maximum or minimum value for μ; otherwise use Table C.) The value for df (the degrees of freedom) is the number of elements in the sample minus one (n − 1).

After locating the t score, the predicted range for the population mean can be calculated using the formula:

Predicted range for the population mean = $\bar{x} \pm \dfrac{s_x}{\sqrt{n}} t$

Summary on Statistical Inference

One process of statistical inference that can be of great use in decision making involves taking data from a sample and from that calculating a predicted range for the population mean. This range shows, to the selected degree of certainty, where the population mean lies. Chapter 4, on testing claims, discusses how to compare this predicted range for the population mean to the mean value claimed by a manufacturer or supplier for a given product, part, etc. If the claimed mean value does not fall in the predicted range, there may be a problem and you may want to reject a shipment or talk further with the supplier. Using data from a sample, you can make more accurate decisions about claims being made for a population using the calculator and statistics.

The steps involved in the process of statistical inference are summarized in the following diagram.

Steps in Analyzing Sample Data, to Calculate the Predicted Range
for the Population Mean:

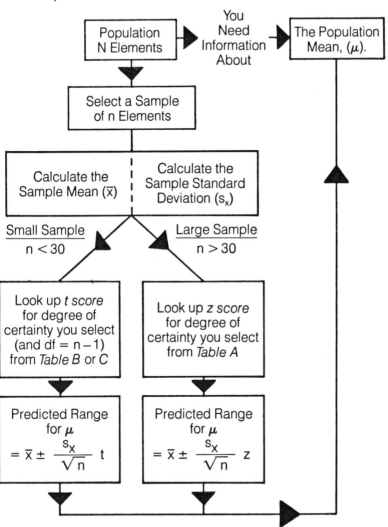

Standard Deviation

To be as accurate as possible, statisticians use two formulas for calculating standard deviation. When calculating the standard deviation of a population (σ) they use the formula:

$$\sigma = \sqrt{\frac{\Sigma_i(x_i - \bar{x})^2}{N}},$$

where N is the number of elements in the population.

NOTE: The symbol Σ_i used here (and elsewhere) means "the sum of". In this case $\Sigma_i(x_i - \bar{x})^2$ means to add all the values of $(x_i - \bar{x})^2$ for i going from 1 to N.

When handling an entire population, enter the data with the Σ+ and 2nd Frq keys, and calculate:

— the population mean (μ) by pressing 2nd Mean

— the standard deviation of the population (σ) by pressing 2nd σn .

When calculating the standard deviation of a sample, (s_x), the formula used is:

$$s_x = \sqrt{\frac{\Sigma_i(x_i - \bar{x})^2}{n - 1}},$$

where n is the number of elements in the sample.

When handling a sample, enter the data with the Σ+ and 2nd Frq keys, and calculate:

— the sample mean ($\bar{x}$) by pressing 2nd Mean

— the sample standard deviation (s_x) by pressing 2nd σn-1 .

The complete reasoning behind the difference in these two calculations is beyond the scope of this book. For values of $n > 30$, the difference between these two calculations becomes very small.

Summary

This chapter has surveyed a large amount of information quite briefly. The other chapters of this book show how to use this information in step-by-step, easy to apply procedures, along with keystroke sequences and sample calculations. Using these powerful methods, with the calculator doing the arithmetic, is quite easy, and does not require studying statistics for years. After seeing these methods actually applied, many of the procedures will become clearer.

The number of symbols used in this book has been kept to a minimum. However, for your reference they are tabulated below. A complete table of all symbols used is also included in the Appendix.

	Population	Sample	Calculator Key Sequence
Number of Elements	N	n	Enter Value of Element, Press $\boxed{\Sigma+}$
Mean	σ	$\bar{x}$	Press $\boxed{2nd}$ ▬▬
	$\sigma = \sqrt{\dfrac{\Sigma_i(x_i - \bar{x})^2}{N}}$	$s_x = \sqrt{\dfrac{\Sigma_i(x_i - \bar{x})^2}{n-1}}$	σ: Press $\boxed{2nd}$ ▬▬ s_x Press $\boxed{2nd}$ ▬▬

$\sigma_{\bar{x}}$ = Standard Deviation of the Sample Means

z = z score for a selected degree of certainty

t = t score for a selected degree of certainty and specific number
   of degrees of freedom (df)

Statistical Information

Summary of Symbols

df — degrees of freedom
F — F number from Table D or E
n — number of elements in a sample
N — number of elements in a population
r — correlation coefficient
r_{test} — test correlation coefficient
Sx_H — standard deviation of the "high" sample
Sx_L — standard deviation of the "low" sample
s_x — standard deviation of a sample
$\sigma_{\bar{x}}$ — standard deviation of sample means
σ — standard deviation of a population
t — t number from Table B or C
x_i — the ith element of a sample or population
$\bar{x}$ — sample mean
μ — population mean
z — z number from Table A

Table A

z Scores

Degree of Certainty	Column I For Checking Only an Upper or Lower Level	Column II For Checking Both an Upper and Lower Level
60	0.26	0.84
65	0.39	0.94
70	0.53	1.04
75	0.68	1.15
80	0.84	1.28
85	1.04	1.44
90	1.28	1.65
95	1.65	1.96
99	2.33	2.58

STATISTICAL INFORMATION

Table B

t Scores

(For Checking <u>Only</u> Upper or Lower Limits)

←———————— Level of Certainty ————————→

Degrees of Freedom (df)	90%	95%	99%	99.5%
1	3.078	6.314	31.821	63.657
2	1.886	2.920	6.965	9.925
3	1.638	2.353	4.541	5.841
4	1.533	2.132	3.747	4.604
5	1.476	2.015	3.365	4.032
6	1.440	1.943	3.143	3.707
7	1.415	1.895	2.998	3.499
8	1.397	1.860	2.896	3.355
9	1.383	1.833	2.821	3.250
10	1.372	1.812	2.764	3.169
11	1.363	1.796	2.718	3.106
12	1.356	1.782	2.681	3.055
13	1.350	1.771	2.650	3.012
14	1.345	1.761	2.624	2.977
15	1.341	1.753	2.602	2.947
16	1.337	1.746	2.583	2.921
17	1.333	1.740	2.567	2.898
18	1.330	1.734	2.552	2.878
19	1.328	1.729	2.539	2.861
20	1.325	1.725	2.528	2.845
21	1.323	1.721	2.518	2.831
22	1.321	1.717	2.508	2.819
23	1.319	1.714	2.500	2.807
24	1.318	1.711	2.492	2.797
25	1.316	1.708	2.485	2.787
26	1.315	1.706	2.479	2.779
27	1.314	1.703	2.473	2.771
28	1.313	1.701	2.467	2.763
29	1.311	1.699	2.462	2.756
30	1.310	1.697	2.457	2.750
40	1.303	1.684	2.423	2.704
60	1.296	1.671	2.390	2.660
120	1.289	1.658	2.358	2.617
∞	1.282	1.645	2.326	2.576

Table C

t Scores
(For Checking Both Upper and Lower Limits)

Level of Certainty

Degrees of Freedom (df)	80%	90%	95%	99%	99.9%
1	3.078	6.314	12.706	63.657	636.619
2	1.886	2.920	4.303	9.925	31.598
3	1.638	2.353	3.182	5.841	12.941
4	1.533	2.132	2.776	4.604	8.610
5	1.476	2.015	2.571	4.032	6.859
6	1.440	1.943	2.447	3.707	5.959
7	1.415	1.895	2.365	3.499	5.405
8	1.397	1.860	2.306	3.355	5.041
9	1.383	1.833	2.262	3.250	4.781
10	1.372	1.812	2.228	3.169	4.587
11	1.363	1.796	2.201	3.106	4.437
12	1.356	1.782	2.179	3.055	4.318
13	1.350	1.771	2.160	3.012	4.221
14	1.345	1.761	2.145	2.977	4.140
15	1.341	1.753	2.131	2.947	4.073
16	1.337	1.746	2.120	2.921	4.015
17	1.333	1.740	2.110	2.898	3.965
18	1.330	1.734	2.101	2.878	3.922
19	1.328	1.729	2.093	2.861	3.883
20	1.325	1.725	2.086	2.845	3.850
21	1.323	1.721	2.080	2.831	3.819
22	1.321	1.717	2.074	2.819	3.792
23	1.319	1.714	2.069	2.807	3.767
24	1.318	1.711	2.064	2.797	3.745
25	1.316	1.708	2.060	2.787	3.725
26	1.315	1.706	2.056	2.779	3.707
27	1.314	1.703	2.052	2.771	3.690
28	1.313	1.701	2.048	2.763	3.674
29	1.311	1.699	2.045	2.756	3.659
30	1.310	1.697	2.042	2.750	3.646
40	1.303	1.684	2.021	2.704	3.551
60	1.296	1.671	2.000	2.660	3.460
120	1.289	1.658	1.980	2.617	3.373
∞	1.282	1.645	1.960	2.576	3.291

Table D **F Values at 95% Level of Certainty**

Degrees of Freedom of the Numerator

Den. df \ Num. df	1	2	3	4	5	6	7	8	9	10	12	15	20	30	60	120	∞
1	161.4	199.5	215.7	224.6	230.2	234.0	236.8	238.9	240.5	241.9	243.9	245.9	248.0	250.1	252.2	253.3	254.3
2	18.51	19.00	19.16	19.25	19.30	19.33	19.35	19.37	19.38	19.40	19.41	19.43	19.45	19.46	19.48	19.49	19.50
3	10.13	9.55	9.28	9.12	9.01	8.94	8.89	8.85	8.81	8.79	8.74	8.70	8.66	8.62	8.57	8.55	8.53
4	7.71	6.94	6.59	6.39	6.26	6.16	6.09	6.04	6.00	5.96	5.91	5.86	5.80	5.75	5.69	5.66	5.63
5	6.61	5.79	5.41	5.19	5.05	4.95	4.88	4.82	4.77	4.74	4.68	4.62	4.56	4.50	4.43	4.40	4.36
6	5.99	5.14	4.76	4.53	4.39	4.28	4.21	4.15	4.10	4.06	4.00	3.94	3.87	3.81	3.74	3.70	3.67
7	5.59	4.74	4.35	4.12	3.97	3.87	3.79	3.73	3.68	3.64	3.57	3.51	3.44	3.38	3.30	3.27	3.23
8	5.32	4.46	4.07	3.84	3.69	3.58	3.50	3.44	3.39	3.35	3.28	3.22	3.15	3.08	3.01	2.97	2.93
9	5.12	4.26	3.86	3.63	3.48	3.37	3.29	3.23	3.18	3.14	3.07	3.01	2.94	2.86	2.79	2.75	2.71
10	4.96	4.10	3.71	3.48	3.33	3.22	3.14	3.07	3.02	2.98	2.91	2.85	2.77	2.70	2.62	2.58	2.54
11	4.84	3.98	3.59	3.36	3.20	3.09	3.01	2.95	2.90	2.85	2.79	2.72	2.65	2.57	2.49	2.45	2.40
12	4.75	3.89	3.49	3.26	3.11	3.00	2.91	2.85	2.80	2.75	2.69	2.62	2.54	2.47	2.38	2.34	2.30
13	4.67	3.81	3.41	3.18	3.03	2.92	2.83	2.77	2.71	2.67	2.60	2.53	2.46	2.38	2.30	2.25	2.21
14	4.60	3.74	3.34	3.11	2.96	2.85	2.76	2.70	2.65	2.60	2.53	2.46	2.39	2.31	2.22	2.18	2.13
15	4.54	3.68	3.29	3.06	2.90	2.79	2.71	2.64	2.59	2.54	2.48	2.40	2.33	2.25	2.16	2.11	2.07
16	4.49	3.63	3.24	3.01	2.85	2.74	2.66	2.59	2.54	2.49	2.42	2.35	2.28	2.19	2.11	2.06	2.01
17	4.45	3.59	3.20	2.96	2.81	2.70	2.61	2.55	2.49	2.45	2.38	2.31	2.23	2.15	2.06	2.01	1.96
18	4.41	3.55	3.16	2.93	2.77	2.66	2.58	2.51	2.46	2.41	2.34	2.27	2.19	2.11	2.02	1.97	1.92
19	4.38	3.52	3.13	2.90	2.74	2.63	2.54	2.48	2.42	2.38	2.31	2.23	2.16	2.07	1.98	1.93	1.88
20	4.35	3.49	3.10	2.87	2.71	2.60	2.51	2.45	2.39	2.35	2.28	2.20	2.12	2.04	1.95	1.90	1.84
21	4.32	3.47	3.07	2.84	2.68	2.57	2.49	2.42	2.37	2.32	2.25	2.18	2.10	2.01	1.92	1.87	1.81
22	4.30	3.44	3.05	2.82	2.66	2.55	2.46	2.40	2.34	2.30	2.23	2.15	2.07	1.98	1.89	1.84	1.78
23	4.28	3.42	3.03	2.80	2.64	2.53	2.44	2.37	2.32	2.27	2.20	2.13	2.05	1.96	1.86	1.81	1.76
24	4.26	3.40	3.01	2.78	2.62	2.51	2.42	2.36	2.30	2.25	2.18	2.11	2.03	1.94	1.84	1.79	1.73
25	4.24	3.39	2.99	2.76	2.60	2.49	2.40	2.34	2.28	2.24	2.16	2.09	2.01	1.92	1.82	1.77	1.71
26	4.23	3.37	2.98	2.74	2.59	2.47	2.39	2.32	2.27	2.22	2.15	2.07	1.99	1.90	1.80	1.75	1.69
27	4.21	3.35	2.96	2.73	2.57	2.46	2.37	2.31	2.25	2.20	2.13	2.06	1.97	1.88	1.79	1.73	1.67
28	4.20	3.34	2.95	2.71	2.56	2.45	2.36	2.29	2.24	2.19	2.12	2.04	1.96	1.87	1.77	1.71	1.65
29	4.18	3.33	2.93	2.70	2.55	2.43	2.35	2.28	2.22	2.18	2.10	2.03	1.94	1.85	1.75	1.70	1.64
30	4.17	3.32	2.92	2.69	2.53	2.42	2.33	2.27	2.21	2.16	2.09	2.01	1.93	1.84	1.74	1.68	1.62
40	4.08	3.23	2.84	2.61	2.45	2.34	2.25	2.18	2.12	2.08	2.00	1.92	1.84	1.74	1.64	1.58	1.51
60	4.00	3.15	2.76	2.53	2.37	2.25	2.17	2.10	2.04	1.99	1.92	1.84	1.75	1.65	1.53	1.47	1.39
120	3.92	3.07	2.68	2.45	2.29	2.17	2.09	2.02	1.96	1.91	1.83	1.75	1.66	1.55	1.43	1.35	1.25
∞	3.84	3.00	2.60	2.37	2.21	2.10	2.01	1.94	1.88	1.83	1.75	1.67	1.57	1.46	1.32	1.22	1.00

Degrees of Freedom of the Denominator

Table E **F Values at 99% Level of Certainty**

Degrees of Freedom of the Numerator

Denominator df	1	2	3	4	5	6	7	8	9	10	12	15	20	30	60	120	∞
1	4052	4999.5	5403	5625	5764	5859	5928	5982	6022	6056	6106	6157	6209	6261	6313	6339	6366
2	98.50	99.00	99.17	99.25	99.30	99.33	99.36	99.37	99.39	99.40	99.42	99.43	99.45	99.47	99.48	99.49	99.50
3	34.12	30.82	29.46	28.71	28.24	27.91	27.67	27.49	27.35	27.23	27.05	26.87	26.69	26.50	26.32	26.22	26.13
4	21.20	18.00	16.69	15.98	15.52	15.21	14.98	14.80	14.66	14.55	14.37	14.20	14.02	13.84	13.65	13.56	13.46
5	16.26	13.27	12.06	11.39	10.97	10.67	10.46	10.29	10.16	10.05	9.89	9.72	9.55	9.38	9.20	9.11	9.02
6	13.75	10.92	9.78	9.15	8.75	8.47	8.26	8.10	7.98	7.87	7.72	7.56	7.40	7.23	7.06	6.97	6.88
7	12.25	9.55	8.45	7.85	7.46	7.19	6.99	6.84	6.72	6.62	6.47	6.31	6.16	5.99	5.82	5.74	5.65
8	11.26	8.65	7.59	7.01	6.63	6.37	6.18	6.03	5.91	5.81	5.67	5.52	5.36	5.20	5.03	4.95	4.86
9	10.56	8.02	6.99	6.42	6.06	5.80	5.61	5.47	5.35	5.26	5.11	4.96	4.81	4.65	4.48	4.40	4.31
10	10.04	7.56	6.55	5.99	5.64	5.39	5.20	5.06	4.94	4.85	4.71	4.56	4.41	4.25	4.08	4.00	3.91
11	9.65	7.21	6.22	5.67	5.32	5.07	4.89	4.74	4.63	4.54	4.40	4.25	4.10	3.94	3.78	3.69	3.60
12	9.33	6.93	5.95	5.41	5.06	4.82	4.64	4.50	4.39	4.30	4.16	4.01	3.86	3.70	3.54	3.45	3.36
13	9.07	6.70	5.74	5.21	4.86	4.62	4.44	4.30	4.19	4.10	3.96	3.82	3.66	3.51	3.34	3.25	3.17
14	8.86	6.51	5.56	5.04	4.69	4.46	4.28	4.14	4.03	3.94	3.80	3.66	3.51	3.35	3.18	3.09	3.00
15	8.68	6.36	5.42	4.89	4.56	4.32	4.14	4.00	3.89	3.80	3.67	3.52	3.37	3.21	3.05	2.96	2.87
16	8.53	6.23	5.29	4.77	4.44	4.20	4.03	3.89	3.78	3.69	3.55	3.41	3.26	3.10	2.93	2.84	2.75
17	8.40	6.11	5.18	4.67	4.34	4.10	3.93	3.79	3.68	3.59	3.46	3.31	3.16	3.00	2.83	2.75	2.65
18	8.29	6.01	5.09	4.58	4.25	4.01	3.84	3.71	3.60	3.51	3.37	3.23	3.08	2.92	2.75	2.66	2.57
19	8.18	5.93	5.01	4.50	4.17	3.94	3.77	3.63	3.52	3.43	3.30	3.15	3.00	2.84	2.67	2.58	2.49
20	8.10	5.85	4.94	4.43	4.10	3.87	3.70	3.56	3.46	3.37	3.23	3.09	2.94	2.78	2.61	2.52	2.42
21	8.02	5.78	4.87	4.37	4.04	3.81	3.64	3.51	3.40	3.31	3.17	3.03	2.88	2.72	2.55	2.46	2.36
22	7.95	5.72	4.82	4.31	3.99	3.76	3.59	3.45	3.35	3.26	3.12	2.98	2.83	2.67	2.50	2.40	2.31
23	7.88	5.66	4.76	4.26	3.94	3.71	3.54	3.41	3.30	3.21	3.07	2.93	2.78	2.62	2.45	2.35	2.26
24	7.82	5.61	4.72	4.22	3.90	3.67	3.50	3.36	3.26	3.17	3.03	2.89	2.74	2.58	2.40	2.31	2.21
25	7.77	5.57	4.68	4.18	3.85	3.63	3.46	3.32	3.22	3.13	2.99	2.85	2.70	2.54	2.36	2.27	2.17
26	7.72	5.53	4.64	4.14	3.82	3.59	3.42	3.29	3.18	3.09	2.96	2.81	2.66	2.50	2.33	2.23	2.13
27	7.68	5.49	4.60	4.11	3.78	3.56	3.39	3.26	3.15	3.06	2.93	2.78	2.63	2.47	2.29	2.20	2.10
28	7.64	5.45	4.57	4.07	3.75	3.53	3.36	3.23	3.12	3.03	2.90	2.75	2.60	2.44	2.26	2.17	2.06
29	7.60	5.42	4.54	4.04	3.73	3.50	3.33	3.20	3.09	3.00	2.87	2.73	2.57	2.41	2.23	2.14	2.03
30	7.56	5.39	4.51	4.02	3.70	3.47	3.30	3.17	3.07	2.98	2.84	2.70	2.55	2.39	2.21	2.11	2.01
40	7.31	5.18	4.31	3.83	3.51	3.29	3.12	2.99	2.89	2.80	2.66	2.52	2.37	2.20	2.02	1.92	1.80
60	7.08	4.98	4.13	3.65	3.34	3.12	2.95	2.82	2.72	2.63	2.50	2.35	2.20	2.03	1.84	1.73	1.60
120	6.85	4.79	3.95	3.48	3.17	2.96	2.79	2.66	2.56	2.47	2.34	2.19	2.03	1.86	1.66	1.53	1.38
∞	6.63	4.61	3.78	3.32	3.02	2.80	2.64	2.51	2.41	2.32	2.18	2.04	1.88	1.70	1.47	1.32	1.00

Degrees of Freedom of the Denominator

Integration: Simpson's Rule

The integral key on the TI-55-II uses Simpson's Rule, which is a method of approximating the definite integral of a function. An integral can be considered as the area under a curve.

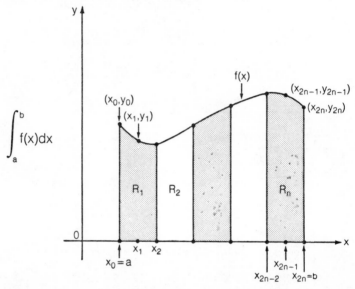

$$\int_a^b f(x)dx$$

The area under the curve may be divided into an even number of subintervals, say 2n subintervals of length $h = (b - a) \div 2n$ with endpoints $x_0 (=a)$, x_1, ... , x_{2n-1}, $x_{2n} (=b)$.

$A_1 = \dfrac{h}{3} (y_0 + 4y_1 + y_2)$ is an approximation of the area of R_1.

Similarly A_2 is an approximation of R_2. Therefore A_n is an approximation of the area of R_n. Then adding $A_1 + A_2 + ... + A_n$ gives an approximation of the area under the curve.

This approximation for definite integrals is stated in Simpson's Rule:

$$\int_a^b f(x)dx = \frac{h}{3} (y_0 + 4y_1 + 2y_2 + ... + 2y_{2n-2} + 4y_{2n-1} + y_{2n})$$

Note that the first and last terms in the parentheses have one for a coefficient. All other "y" terms with even subscripts have two for a coefficient, and all "y" terms with odd subscripts have four for a coefficient.

Error Conditions

The display shows "Error" when overflow or underflow occurs or when an improper operation is requested. When this occurs, no entry from the keyboard except [OFF] is accepted until [ON/c] is pressed. Pressing [ON/c] clears the error condition and all pending operations. You must then determine what caused the error and rekey the entry to avoid the problem.

The following list the circumstances which cause "Error" to be displayed. The first section shows the general conditions. They do not affect statistical data points which have been entered. The second section lists errors due to statistical operations. They clear all data points and reset the statistics mode as if [2nd] [CSR] had been pressed.

Section 1—General Error Conditions

1. Number entry or calculation result (including in memories) is outside the range $\pm 1 \times 10^{-99}$ to $\pm 9.9999999 \times 10^{99}$.
2. Multiplying a number greater than 1×10^{99} by another number may cause an error condition.
3. Dividing a number by zero.
4. Calculating [log], [lnx], or [1/x] of zero or calculating the 0th root of any number or zero to the zero power.
5. Calculating [log], [lnx], a power or root of a negative number.
6. Inverse of sine or cosine (arcsine or arccosine) when the absolute value in the display is greater than 1.
7. Tangent of 90° or 270°, $\pi \div 2$ radians or $3\pi \div 2$ radians, 100 grads or 300 grads, or their rotational multiples such as 450°.
8. Having more than 15 open levels of parentheses or more than 4 pending operations.
9. Factorial of any number except a non-negative integer less than 70.
10. Using [RCL], [STO], or [EXC] for a memory that is not defined by the current partition.
11. When using memory arithmetic, following [STO] with two memory arithmetic operations instead of an operation and a valid user data memory number.
12. When using memory arithmetic, following [RCL] or [EXC] with an operation instead of a valid user data memory number.

13. Calculating the percent change where the old value is equal to zero.
14. Using an argument outside the range given in Accuracy Information for the logarithmic and trigonometric functions.
15. Integrating with fewer than three user data memories or with no program steps.
16. Finding permutations or combinations with more than three digits after the decimal point.
17. Calculating rectangular to polar conversions with values for x and y such that the sum of their squares exceeds the upper or lower limit of the calculator, or x and y both equal zero.

Section 2—Statistical Error Conditions

1. Calculating **On-1** with only one data point.
2. Entering a data point such that $x \leq \pm 1 \times 10^{-50}$ or $x \geq \pm 1 \times 10^{50}$.
3. Entering a series of data points such that the sum of their squares exceeds the upper or lower limit of the calculator.
4. Entering more than 99,999 data points.
5. Making it so that there are zero or fewer data points by removing data points with 2nd Σ− or 2nd Frq 2nd Σ− .
6. Calculating the slope, intercept, correlation, x', or y' of a line that parallels the y-axis (vertical line).
7. Calculating the correlation or x' of a line that parallels the x-axis (horizontal line).
8. Calculating the slope, intercept, correlation, x', or y', with only one data point entered.

Accuracy Information

Each calculation produces an 11-digit result which is rounded to an 8-digit standard display. The 5/4 rounding technique used adds 1 to the least significant digit in the display if the next non-displayed digit is five or more. If this digit is less than five, no rounding occurs. In the absence of these extra digits, inaccurate results would frequently be displayed, such as

$1 \div 3 \times 3 = 0.9999999$

Because of rounding, the answer is given as 1, but is internally equal to 0.9999999999.

The higher order mathematical functions use iterative calculations. The cumulative error from these calculations in most cases is maintained beyond the 8-digit display so that no inaccuracy is displayed. Most calculations are accurate to ± 1 in the last displayed digit. There are a few instances in the solution of high order functions where display accuracy begins to deteriorate as the function approaches a discontinuous or undefined point. For example, the tangent of 87° is accurate for all displayed digits. However, the tangent of 89.99999° is accurate to only three places. Another example is when the y^x function has a y value that approaches 1 and an x value that is a very large positive or negative number. The displayed result for 1.05^{-160} is accurate for all displayed digits, while 1.0000005^{-16000} is accurate to only five places.

Trigonometric values can be calculated for angles greater than one revolution. As long as the trigonometric function result is displayed in normal form rather than in scientific or engineering notation, all displayed digits are accurate for any angle from −36,000° to 36,000° and −40,000 to 40,000 grads. The equivalent range in radians ($\pm 200\pi$) is comparable to degrees and grads in accuracy except at rotation multiples of π and $\pi \div 2$. The rounded value of π limits accuracy at these points. In general, the accuracy decreases one digit for each decade outside this range.

D

ACCURACY INFORMATION

The following gives the limits within which the display must be when calculating certain functions.

Function	Limit
$\sin^{-1} x$, $\cos^{-1} x$	$-1 \leq x \leq 1$
$\sinh x$, $\cosh x$	$0 \leq |x| \leq 227.95592$
$\sinh^{-1} x$	$-10^{50} < x < -10^{-50}$, $10^{-50} < x < 10^{50}$, $x = 0$
$\cosh^{-1} x$	$1 \leq x < 10^{50}$
$\tanh^{-1} x$	$-1 < x < 1$
$\ln x$, $\log x$	$1 \times 10^{-99} \leq x < 1 \times 10^{100}$
e^{x}	$-227.95592 \leq x \leq 230.25850$
10^{x}	$-99 \leq x < 100$
$x!$	$0 \leq x \leq 69$ where x is an integer

The following gives the range of results of the inverse trigonometric functions.

Arc Function	Range of Resultant Angle
arcsin x	0 to 90°, $\pi \div 2$ radians, or 100G
arcsin −x	0 to −90°, $-\pi \div 2$ radians, or −100G
arccos x	0 to 90°, $\pi \div 2$ radians, or 100G
arccos −x	90° to 180°, $\pi \div 2$ to π radians, or 100G to 200G
arctan x	0 to 90°, $\pi \div 2$ radians, or 100G
arctan −x	0 to −90°, $-\pi \div 2$ radians, or −100G

SERVICE AND WARRANTY INFORMATION

In Case of Difficulty

In the event that you have difficulty with your calculator, the following instructions will help you to analyze the problem. You may be able to correct your calculator problem without returning the unit to a service facility. If the suggested remedies are not successful, contact the Consumer Relations Department by mail or telephone (refer to WARRANTY PERFORMANCE). Please describe in detail the symptoms of your calculator.

Symptom	Solution
Display is blank, shows erroneous results, flashes erratic numbers, or grows dim.	The battery may be discharged. Insert new batteries using the instructions in BATTERY REPLACEMENT.

If the above procedure does not correct the difficulty, return the calculator prepaid to the applicable Service Facility listed under Warranty Performance.

Battery Replacement

NOTE: The calculator cannot hold data in its user data memories or mode registers when the batteries are removed or become discharged.

The calculator uses 2 of any of the following batteries for up to 750 hours of operation: Panasonic LR-44, Ray-O-Vac RW-82, Union Carbide (Eveready) A-76, or the equivalent. For up to 2000 hours of operation use Mallory 10L14, Union Carbide (Eveready) 357, Panasonic WL-14, Toshiba G-13, Ray-O-Vac RW-42, or the equivalent.

1. Turn the calculator off. Place a small screwdriver, paper clip, or other similar instrument into the slot and gently lift the battery cover.

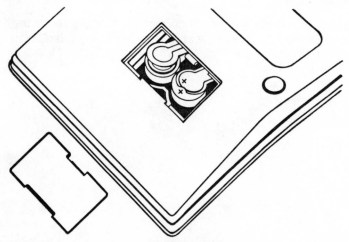

2. Remove the discharged batteries and install new ones as shown. Be careful not to crease the film contacts while installing the new batteries. Be sure the film contacts are positioned to lay on top of the batteries after the batteries are installed.

3. Replace the cover top edge first, then gently press until the bottom of the cover snaps into place.

4. Press [ON/C], [2nd] **Part** [8], [OFF], [ON/C], [ON/C], [2nd] **CSR**, [2nd] **Part** [8], [2nd] **CM**, and [ON/C]. The display then shows 0 and DEG and the calculator is ready to be used.

One-Year Limited Warranty

THIS TEXAS INSTRUMENTS ELECTRONIC CALCULATOR WAR-
RANTY EXTENDS TO THE ORIGINAL CONSUMER PURCHASER OF
THE PRODUCT.

WARRANTY DURATION: This calculator is warranted to the original
consumer purchaser for a period of one year from the original purchase date.

WARRANTY COVERAGE: This calculator is warranted against defec-
tive materials or workmanship. **THIS WARRANTY DOES NOT COVER
BATTERIES AND IS VOID IF THE PRODUCT HAS BEEN DAMAGED
BY ACCIDENT, UNREASONABLE USE, NEGLECT, IMPROPER SER-
VICE OR OTHER CAUSE NOT ARISING OUT OF DEFECTS IN MATE-
RIAL OR WORKMANSHIP.**

**WARRANTY DISCLAIMERS: ANY IMPLIED WARRANTIES ARIS-
ING OUT OF THIS SALE, INCLUDING BUT NOT LIMITED TO THE IM-
PLIED WARRANTIES OF MERCHANTABILITY AND FITNESS FOR A
PARTICULAR PURPOSE, ARE LIMITED IN DURATION TO THE
ABOVE ONE YEAR PERIOD. TEXAS INSTRUMENTS SHALL NOT BE
LIABLE FOR LOSS OF USE OF THE CALCULATOR OR OTHER INCI-
DENTAL OR CONSEQUENTIAL COSTS, EXPENSES, OR DAMAGES
INCURRED BY THE CONSUMER OR ANY OTHER USER.** Some states
do not allow the exclusion or limitation of implied warranties or conse-
quential damages, so the above limitations or exclusions may not
apply to you.

LEGAL REMEDIES: This warranty gives you specific legal rights, and
you may also have other rights that vary from state to state.

WARRANTY PERFORMANCE: During the above one year warranty
period your TI calculator will either be repaired or replaced with a reconditioned comparable model (at TI's option) when the product is returned,
postage prepaid, to a Texas Instruments Service Facility listed below. In
the event of replacement with a reconditioned model, the replacement
product will continue the warranty of the original calculator or 6 months,
whichever is longer. Other than the postage requirement, no charge will
be made for such repair, adjustment, and/or replacement.

If the calculator is out of warranty, service rates in effect at the time of return will be charged. Please include information on the difficulty experi-
enced with the calculator as well as return address information including
name, address, city, state, and zip code. The shipment should be
carefully packaged and adequately protected against shock and
rough handling.

Texas Instruments Consumer Service Facilities

U. S. Residents:
Texas Instruments Service Facility
P. O. Box 2500
Lubbock, Texas 79408

Canadian customers only:
Geophysical Services Incorporated
41 Shelley Road
Richmond Hill, Ontario, Canada L4C5G4

NOTE: The P.O.Box number listed for the Lubbock Service Facility is for
United States parcel post shipments only. If you use another carrier, the
street address is:

Texas Instruments Incorporated
2305 University Avenue
Lubbock, TX 79415

CALCULATOR EXCHANGE CENTERS

If your calculator requires service, instead of returning the unit to your dealer or to a service facility for repair, you may elect to exchange the calculator for a factory-rebuilt calculator of the same model (or equivalent model specified by TI) by bringing the calculator in person to one of the exchange centers which have been established across the United States. No charge will be made for the exchange with proof-of-purchase during the first 90 days. The exchanged unit will be in warranty for the remainder of the original warranty period or for 6 months, whichever is longer. A handling fee will be charged for exchange after 90 days from the date of purchase. Out-of-warranty exchanges will be charged at the rates in effect at the time of the exchange. To determine if there is an exchange center in your locality, look for Texas Instruments Incorporated Exchange Center in the white pages of your telephone directory or look under the Calculator and Adding Machine heading in the yellow pages. Please call the exchange center for the availability of your model. Write or call the Consumer Relations Department for further details and the location of the nearest exchange center.

MAILING INSTRUCTIONS

Enclose a written explanation of the problem with your calculator. Be sure to include your name and return address.

Wrap your calculator in tissue or similar soft packing material and enclose it in a strong, crushproof mailing carton. If you use the original display box for mailing, it cannot be returned to you.

To protect your calculator from theft, do not write "calculator" on the outside of the package. Send your calculator to the appropriate address listed in WARRANTY PERFORMANCE.

Texas Instruments strongly recommends that you insure the product for value prior to mailing.

IF YOU NEED SERVICE INFORMATION

If you have questions concerning calculator repair, accessory purchase or the basic functions of your calculator, please call our Consumer Relations Department at (800) 858-1802 (toll free within the contiguous United States except Texas) or (800) 692-1353 (within Texas). If outside the contiguous United States call (806) 741-2646. We regret we cannot accept collect calls at this number.

SERVICE AND WARRANTY INFORMATION

FOR TECHNICAL ASSISTANCE

For technical questions such as programming, specific calculator applications, etc., you can call (806) 747-3841. We regret that this is not a toll-free number, and we cannot accept collect calls. As an alternative, you can write to:

Texas Instruments Consumer Relations
P. O. Box 53
Lubbock, Texas 79408

California and Oregon: Consumers in California and Oregon may contact the following Texas Instruments offices for additional assistance or information.

Texas Instruments Consumer Service
831 South Douglas Street
El Segundo, California 90245
(213) 973-1803

Texas Instruments
Consumer Service
6700 Southwest 105th St.
Kristin Square, Suite 110
Beaverton, Oregon 97005
(503) 643-6758

Because of the number of suggestions which come to Texas Instruments from many sources, containing both new and old ideas, Texas Instruments will consider such suggestions only if they are freely given to Texas Instruments. It is the policy of Texas Instruments to refuse to receive any suggestions in confidence. Therefore, if you wish to share your suggestions with Texas Instruments, or if you wish us to review any calculator program key sequence which you have developed, please include the following in your letter:

"All of the information forwarded herewith is presented to Texas Instruments on a nonconfidential, nonobligatory basis; no relationship, confidential or otherwise, expressed or implied, is established with Texas Instruments by this presentation. Texas Instruments may use, copyright, distribute, publish, reproduce, or dispose of the information in any way without compensation to me."

Bibliography

Anthony, Robert N. and Glen A. Welsch. *Fundamentals of Management Accounting.* Homewood, Illinois: Richard D. Irwin, 1974.

Anthony, Robert N. and James S. Reece. *Management Accounting Text and Cases.* Fifth edition. Homewood, Illinois: Richard D Irwin, 1975.

Chou, Ya-lun. *Statistical Analysis.* New York: Holt, Rinehart and Winston, 1975.

Ferguson, George A. *Statistical Analysis in Psychology and Education.* New York: McGraw-Hill Book Company, 1966.

Freund, John E. *Mathematical Statistics.* Englewood Cliffs, New Jersey: Printice-Hall, Inc., 1962.

Hummel, Paul M. and Charles Seebeck. *Mathematics of Finance.* New York: McGraw-Hill Book Company, 1971.

LaMont, M. Dean, Lane L. Douglas and Ralph A. Oliva. *Calculator Decision-Making Sourcebook.* Dallas: Texas Instruments Incorporated, 1977

Oliva, Ralph A., M. Dean LaMont and Linda R. Fowler. *Student Calculator Math Book.* Dallas: Texas Instruments Incorporated, 1980

Weston, J. Fred and Eugene F. Brigham; *Essentials of Managerial Finance.* Third Edition. Hinsdale, Illinois: The Dryden Press, 1974.

White, Harvey E. *Introduction to College Physics.* New York: Van Nostrand-Reinhold Company, 1969.

Index

The following index should be supplemented by looking at the Key
Index inside the front cover.

NOTES

NOTES

NOTES

NOTES

NOTES